HERE I AM!
about the author

Russell Stannard is Professor of Physics at the Open University, Milton Keynes, and Vice-president of the Institute of Physics. He has travelled widely in Europe and the United States of America, researching high energy nuclear physics. In 1968 he received the Templeton UK project award and has recently spent a year in America as Visiting Fellow at the Center of Theological Inquiry, Princeton.

Married with four children of his own and three step-children, he believes that the elements of physics can and should be introduced to children in an exciting and accessible way. *The Time and Space of Uncle Albert*, his first book for young readers, was shortlisted for both The Science Book Award and the Whitbread Award (Children's category). *Black Holes and Uncle Albert* is his second book which explores Einstein's theories and can be read as a companion volume or on its own *Here I Am!* is his response to the challenging question: can science and religious belief co-exist in the modern world?

HERE I AM!
Russell Stannard

illustrated by
Jonathan Pugh

faber and faber
LONDON · BOSTON

My thanks
to John Hull, who suggested I should now try to do for
God what I had earlier done for Einstein; to Maggi, my
wife, for her creative insights; to the children of
Beaconsfield School, Burnham Grammar School, and
Putteridge High School, Luton, for pointing out to me why
the earlier drafts of the book were not much good, and for
showing me how they might be improved.

First published in 1992
by Faber and Faber Limited
3 Queen Square London WC1N 3AU
This paperback edition first published in 1993

Printed in England by Clays Ltd, St Ives plc

A CIP record for this book is available from the British Library.

ISBN 0 571 16829 9

2 4 6 8 10 9 7 5 3 1

Contents

1 Well, If It Isn't . . .

'Hi Sam! How's it going?'

The first of the messages. There I was playing about on the computer, when all of a sudden, the screen went blank, and this writing came up.

How's *what* going, I wondered. Where's the manual?

More writing . . .

'Life and all that. What do you make of it?'

I don't believe this . . . Life?

It sounded like an educational programme – the sort Dad *thought* I'd be using the computer for when he got it at Christmas. *Electronic Learning Interface* – that's what it's called. *ELI* for short. I just use it for typing up my homework – and for the games . . .

'Is anybody there?'

Oh, lor! A computer virus! That must be it. A hacker! A hacker getting at my programmes, throwing up stupid messages . . .

'Hello! Are these messages getting through? Answer: Y/N.'

I'd better get Dad. Oh, no – he's not home

tonight . . . What should I do? Play along with the hacker for a bit? See if I can find out who he is?

I tapped in Y for 'yes'.

'Good. So what's on your mind? Why call me up?'

Call him up? What's he on about?

'I didn't call you up,' I tapped back at him.

'Yes, you did. You called up the I AM routine.'

I hadn't a clue what he meant.

'What I AM routine?' I typed.

'The name of my programme. You keyed in I AM. That automatically overrules what you were doing before. Puts you straight through to me.'

'But I didn't. I was . . . just mucking about.'

'Mucking about? What exactly . . .?'

I didn't like to say. I had got fed up typing properly, so was just having a bit of fun – bashing away with all fingers (instead of the usual two) – pretending I could type fast like Mum. I had all these foreign-looking words pouring on to the screen.

'I was hitting the keys,' I replied.

'Which ones? Which keys?'

'Not sure. Any keys.'

'Oh . . . Oh, I see! You were hitting keys at random. That explains it. You must have hit I-blank-A-M without knowing. Pity. Thought I was in for a chat. Anyway, suit yourself . . .'

Once more the screen was flooded by my 'foreign' words. The messages had gone.

What on Earth was that all about, I wondered. Chatting to a hacker. Could have been quite interesting, I suppose . . .

'About to quit the system. Last chance: do you want a chat? Y/N.'

He – whoever he might be – was back! Without stopping to think, I leant forward and pressed *Y*.

'Good.'

There was an awkward pause. Then . . .

'Fancy a game?'

'Which one?' I replied, and brought up the games menu.

'Not one of those. No, we're going to play with ideas – the BIG questions – those for which no one can be sure of the answers, or even whether there are answers at all.'

What *have* I got myself into, I wondered.

'Do you realize how old I am?' I asked.

'Never too young to make a start. Tomorrow – who knows? Forget to look both ways and you get run down. Curtains. Life over and you never even knew what it was about!'

'Well, you'd better keep it interesting – and simple. I know where the "Escape" key is.'

'Fair enough. By the way, this computer of yours, can it make noises?'

'Sound effects, you mean?'

'Yes. Explosions, whistles – when you're playing.'

'Of course. It's not on now. Mum says it makes too much of a racket.'

'Well, switch it on, will you. I want to try something.'

I did as he asked, and sat waiting. Suddenly:

'How's that? Can you hear me?'

The computer spoke to me! I was stunned. It had never done that before.

'Hello! Are you receiving me?'

'Er. Ye-es,' I stammered.

'Great! I can hear you too.'

He . . . he can *hear* me? But that's impossible. There'd have to be a microphone – in the computer. It didn't say anything about that in the manual. Did it? A microphone? What would that be for? Oh no! I know what's happened: the computer's been *bugged*! Hacking, now bugging. And that means . . . that means someone's been listening in to everything that's been going on up here!

'It'll be quicker this way without you having to do all that typing,' said the hacker. 'So. What do you want to talk about?'

I didn't know what to say. I was still shocked.

Who have I been talking to up here recently, I asked myself. What did I say to them?

'I . . . I don't know,' I muttered.

'Well, let's have a think,' he said. 'Yes. I know. How about a trip? Fancy a little trip?'

'A what? A *trip* did you say? Sorry. What . . . ?'

'Yes, a trip. How about a quick tour round the Universe?'

4

'Do WHAT?' I exclaimed.

'Well, why not? The meaning of life and all that – how you fit into everything. Can't do better than start by taking a look at what's around you. Won't take long.'

'But how?' I asked.

'I'll show you . . .'

With that, a picture came up on the screen. Not the usual cartoon sort you get with computer games. A TV-type picture. It showed the Earth from outer space – you know the thing I mean – blue globe, white clouds. At least . . . when I say it was a TV-type picture, it was better than that – much better. I don't know what it was, but there was something very *real* about it. Perhaps it was because it was late and had gone dark. I hadn't really noticed, banging away on the computer. The room light wasn't on, so the only light came from the screen. Anyway, there seemed to be an extra brightness about the picture. It was so clear and realistic I felt as though . . . well, I felt as though I had been drawn *into* it! Yes, that's it. I felt I had passed through the computer screen and was actually hovering in space above the Earth!

'OK, you know what that is,' said the hacker. 'Time to begin our journey. Hold tight!'

And we were off. Whoosh! The Earth disappeared into the distance. We passed one planet after another. Panning round I got blinded. The Sun!

'Sorry! Should have warned you,' he said.

I blinked.

'Any idea what it's made of? The Sun?' asked the hacker.

'Er . . . it's a planet. A hot planet,' I replied.

'No, not really. Gas. A ball of very hot gas – a hundred times the diameter of the Earth.'

We continued our journey outwards. After a while I could no longer see the planets; even the Sun looked small and faint. The sky turned inky black – the blackness of night. As my eyes got used to the darkness, I began to notice the stars. Before long, the Sun had shrunk to a dot – just a tiny dot in the sky.

'The Sun,' I said. 'It looks just like a star now.'

'It *is* a star,' said the hacker. 'That's all it is: just an ordinary star. It only looks special from the Earth because it's closer.'

'You're saying *all* stars are balls of fire – huge ones?' I asked.

'That's right.'

I began wondering who the hacker might be. Obviously someone who knew some science. Miss Francis, perhaps? She's my science teacher. No. That would be stupid.

I noticed the stars were no longer spread out evenly over the sky. To start with they had been all around me; I had been in the middle of them. But now I seemed to have come out of them. I was looking back at them. From here I could see that they were gathered together in a great swirling bunch – like a huge Catherine Wheel slowly turning about its centre.

'The Galaxy,' announced my guide. '100,000 million stars. From here you won't be able to make out your Sun any more.'

Still we journeyed on. The Galaxy was left far behind – just a faint smudge in the sky. Only now did I notice the other smudges. They were everywhere you looked.

'Those,' I said. 'They look like galaxies too.'

'That's right: 100,000 million of them – the same as the number of stars in each one of them. Mind-blowing, isn't it? *Your* mind, I mean. It doesn't blow mine, of course. Yes, I must say I'm rather proud of it all.'

Proud of it all? What did that mean?

'Yes, that's one of the ways I express myself . . .'

'Sorry?' I interrupted.

'The Universe tells you something about *me*. It's the way it is because I'm the kind of God I am . . .'

'Kind of God?'

'It's like standing outside a big posh house. You don't have to be a genius to guess who lives there. He must have pots of money for a start, right? A bit of a show-off perhaps. Or, he could be like me: he just wanted to build something big and beautiful. The Universe lets people know of my power and majesty . . .'

'Hold on. What are you on about? You're

saying you're . . . *God*?'

'Er . . . yes. Yes, I'm God. Didn't you know? Sorry, I should . . .'

'GOD!' I exploded.

'Yes. That's right. I thought . . .'

Oh boy, have I got a nutcase here, I muttered to myself. But two can play at this . . .

'Well, what a pity, God,' I said. 'You've picked the wrong one. It just so happens I don't believe in God.'

'You . . . you don't . . .? Why ever not?'

He was beginning to annoy me.

'I've grown out of it,' I declared.

'Grown out of it?! How can you do that?'

'Easy,' I replied. 'When you're little – and don't know any better – you just believe what your parents say: God, Father Christmas, the lot. But now I think for myself. What I say is: where's this God supposed to be? Where's the proof?'

'Oh. So who do you think's talking to you now?' he asked.

'How should I know? Someone who breaks into other people's programmes. Some *human being* type of person. A hacker. You hack into other people's programmes and ruin their computers.'

'A hacker, eh? The Great Hacker in the Sky – breaking into people's lives. Has a certain ring to it. Never been called that before. I like it.'

'Oh, come off it! Stop messing about,' I

demanded. 'Who are you? *Really.*'

'Sam. I've told you. I'm God. I've just been taking you on a trip round my Universe. I *made* it. That's why I was showing it to you. I created it. I created everything.'

Right, I thought. I'll get you . . .

'OK, God. If you made the world, who made YOU?'

'Me? But you can't ask that,' he replied.

'Of course, I can. I just did.'

'But it doesn't make any sense,' he said.

'Of course, it makes sense. Stop dodging . . .'

'Have you stopped kicking your cat?'

'Eh? Kick . . .? Kick my cat, did you say? I don't kick my cat! Who's been saying . . .?'

'Don't dodge the question,' he demanded. 'Yes or no. Have you stopped kicking the cat?'

'But I *can't* . . .' I protested. 'I've *never* kicked my cat, so how can I *stop* doing something I've never even started?'

'Exactly,' said the hacker. 'Some questions are like that. They *sound* all right, but they're not. That's how it is with the question you asked me. Nobody made me because I'm not something or someone who *can* be made. I am the source. I simply . . . AM.'

'Well,' I said, changing my line. 'What are you doing these days – now that you're unemployed? Signing on at the Job Centre?'

'What? Sorry . . . I didn't get that . . .'

'Well, you created everything – got all this

Universe going, right? So that's it. It just runs itself now. You aren't needed any more.'

'Not needed! You don't create a world and then just go on holiday! Who do you think stops the Universe from disappearing? Who *keeps* it in existence?'

'Why should it disappear? It doesn't need anyone to keep it in existence.'

'Who told you *that*? I've a good mind to pull the plug on you for a start. You'd soon see how long you could exist without me.'

'No, I wouldn't. If you made me go out of existence I wouldn't be around to know I had been wrong. Ha!'

He laughed. That just about proved he was a hacker. Well, who ever heard of a real God laughing? In any case, you could tell all along it was just a hacker – from the way he talked. God's supposed to talk fierce – always telling you off.

'Look, Sam,' said the hacker. 'I am into *everything* that exists. It's a bit like being an author. An author doesn't just write the first sentence of the story and then leave the rest to write itself . . .'

'Hold on. A story? What are you saying now? I'm just a character in a story – a story you've made up. Is that it?'

'In a way, yes.'

'Rubbish! I don't need any "author" to decide what I shall think and do.'

'Good point. Dead right. That's what's so great about writing stories – *good* stories. The characters come *alive*; they take on a life of their own. The author starts off thinking he'll make them do this, or do that – but then he realizes such a person wouldn't do anything of the sort, they just wouldn't. So he has to give way; he has to write it differently. What comes out is a funny kind of mixture: what the author puts into it, but also what comes out of the characters themselves. You have to have an author – obviously – to write it down. And anyone reading the story can tell it's a story by that particular author; it has a certain style to it. But that doesn't stop the characters enjoying a life of their own *within* the story. It's not *bad* being a character, you know,' he declared. 'Some characters are more famous than their authors. I enjoy being a character . . .'

'You? A character? But you just said you were the *author*. You can't be. . .'

'I'm both. I'm the Author of the story, but I'm also a character in the story. It's a story about *me* – living alongside people, working with them, sharing their troubles and joys . . .'

'Look,' I interrupted. 'This is stupid. I don't believe a word of it. There isn't a God and that's that. It's not that I'm *against* the idea. Not like Paul – my brother. He can't *stand* religion. In fact, I'd quite *like* to believe in God. But I can't. There's no proof. That's what I keep telling

Mum, and Lizzie – she's my sister. As for the Universe, I couldn't care less where it came from. Makes no difference to me.'

'No difference!' cried the hacker loudly.

Suddenly, I was back in my bedroom. When I say 'back in my bedroom' I don't mean I had actually left it. Of course not. It just *felt* as if I had . . . well, as if I had got back . . . from outer space.

Oh, no. Is that Mum I can hear? On the stairs? The noise and all that? The idiot!

'Keep your voice down,' I whispered angrily. 'I'm not supposed to have this thing on.'

'Sorry,' he said quietly.

We listened.

'Everything all right?' he asked.

All was silent – apart from the faint hum of the computer's fan.

'I think so,' I said. 'But *don't* do that again.'

'Sorry, I'll try and remember. But you do say some odd things. You can't *really* think that, can you?' he resumed. '*No difference*?'

'Why not?'

'Well . . . If the world came into existence on its own – if none of it had been made by me – you'd . . . you'd just be a freak of nature. You'd be an accident – lost in all that space out there.'

'So? What's wrong with that?' I said. 'That's *exactly* what I'm thinking. I'm nobody. I'm one out of billions of people, stuck on an ordinary planet, going round an ordinary star, in an ordinary galaxy. You can't be more *ordinary* than that. Not that I mind. Well, not really. I'd *like* to feel important, sure. Who wouldn't? But if I'm not . . . OK . . . I can live with that.'

For a while the hacker was silent. Then he said,

'Well done. That was well said.'

'Well done?' I asked suspiciously.

'Sure. I like people to be honest. You can't get anywhere with these big questions unless you're honest with yourself.'

'So it doesn't matter whether I believe in God or not – provided I'm being honest?'

'Certainly not. I never said that. If I exist and I created you, I must have had a reason for it. There's a *purpose* behind your life. You're *not* just an accident thrown up by chance. We can't both be right: either life has a purpose, or it doesn't.'

'You're saying I have to believe in you – believe in *God* – so as to have a purpose to my life? I don't go along . . .'

'No, no, I'm not saying that – well, not exactly. You can always *decide* on a purpose for your life. You can decide to work hard to be rich, or famous; you can fight for animal rights, or the Green movement. There are no end of causes. Some are good. But if I'm right, your life *already has a purpose*. Another thing,' he added, 'if I created you, you're *not* ordinary as you were saying. You are *important*.'

13

'Huh! How do you make that out?'

'Well, just think about it. I'm talking to you, right? WHO's talking to you? The creator of all the galaxies out there – the Universe – the creator of all *that* takes a personal interest in *you*! Anyway. That's enough for one evening. School tomorrow. We can carry on some other time. You know how to get hold of me now . . .'

'Er . . . no,' I said in confusion. 'No, I don't. How . . .?'

'Just key in *I AM*.'

'*I AM*? But why that?'

'It's my name,' he replied.

'Your name? Your name's "God" – *if* you were God, that is.'

'Yes, most people call me "God", but in the olden days, in the Bible, they called me "Yahweh" or "Jehovah" – it means "I am".'

'But how come you have a name like that?' I asked.

'Because I created everything. In the beginning there was just me. So, I called myself *I AM*.'

'Silly name, if you ask me.'

'No worse than "Sam".'

'What's wrong with "Sam"?' I asked angrily.

'For a start, it's only one letter different from my name. One letter: big deal,' he said. 'Besides, don't people sometimes wonder whether you're a girl or a boy – a "Samantha" or a "Samuel"?'

2 Take a Bucket of Slime . . .

Got told off this morning! Day-dreaming in class. Wasn't actually; I was thinking about what had happened yesterday on the computer. Well . . . it's only natural, isn't it? I haven't told anybody about it yet. Though it did almost slip out when I asked Premikar if anything odd ever happened with her computer. She wanted to know what kind of 'odd' I meant.

Then there was Sooty. She's done it at last. Sooty's our cat. She's been eyeing the new bird's nest in the tree in the garden for some time now. But that hadn't bothered us. There was no way she could get up to it. But then this afternoon, just as we got back from school, one of the baby birds fell out on to the garden path. In no time, Sooty pounced. A flurry of black fur and feathers, and it was over. Disgusting, really. It's not as though she could have been hungry. That started Lizzie crying. Crying! And she's two years older than me. She's still upset – went straight to her room instead of watching telly; missed today's episode of *Neighbours*. I was upset too, but I'd never do *that*.

As for the hacker, I had decided not to call him up again. Well, he was so full of himself. He was bound to expect me to call him. So by *not* calling him, I'd show him who was in charge of my life. Author, indeed! But then Miss Francis told us today about EVOLUTION. I just *had* to find out what this supposed God had to say about *that*!

'Hold it right there,' I said, as soon as I got through to him. 'So what's all this about the Bible getting caught out, eh?'

'Caught out? What do you mean?' he asked.

'I mean Darwin. Evolution. I take it you've heard of them?'

'Yes, I've heard of them. So what?'

'What do you mean – so what? All that Adam and Eve stuff – it isn't true. That's so what! A load of rubbish. And that's just for starters – that's what you find on the very first pages of the Bible. So what does that say about the rest of it?'

'Oh dear,' murmured the hacker wearily. 'Not *another* one worried about evolution. Honestly, I don't see what the problem is. Take a bucket of slime; warm it in the sunlight; leave to stand for 4,500 million years. Bingo! A human being. Great idea. OK. It doesn't sound likely – not put like that. Can't really blame people like Lizzie for sticking to Adam and Eve. But that's what the scientists say, and generally it pays to go along with them – where scientific questions are concerned.'

Hmmm, I thought to myself. So, he's heard Lizzie is religious – and that she believes in Adam and Eve. This hacker certainly seems to know us pretty well. Sounds as if he's someone at school – or from Lizzie's Church Youth Club. That would tie up. The people there would like it if they could get me to believe in God. Carry on like this and he'll soon give himself away. Mind you, could be a girl, I suppose. Meanwhile . . .

'What's all this about a bucket of slime?' I asked. 'Miss Francis didn't say anything about that. I thought evolution was about us descending from monkeys. That's what *she* said.'

'Are you sure? The theory says you and the apes descended from the same ancestors – not that you came from apes. It's not quite the same thing. How much do you know about evolution?'

'Give us a chance! We only started it today. Not much – but enough. Enough to know that the Bible is not to be trusted.'

'Like a quick run down on it? Just so we can be sure . . .'

A picture came up on the screen. Like the first time, I was startled by its brightness. It was so real. There were leaves and branches; I was in the middle of some bushes. Not really, of course. I wasn't there – I was just watching. But that's how it felt. I felt for all the world as though I was there. I suppose it's a bit like being hypnotized . . .

From where I was, I looked out at a field. Not exactly a field; it was too big for that. A big open area of grass and some trees. There was a herd of deer, like the deer I saw on that visit to Woburn Safari Park last birthday. They were quietly grazing taking no notice.

Suddenly, a twig snapped – right next to me. The deer pricked up their ears and looked startled. I then got the shock of my life. Out of the bushes bounded this LEOPARD! It must have been crouching there all the time no more than a few yards away! Talk about scared! The deer were frightened too. Took to their heels, scattering in all directions. The leopard gave chase, homing in on one of them. He caught up with it and . . . Well you can guess the rest.

'Did you see that, Sam?' asked the hacker in a low voice.

'See it? Of course I saw it!' I whispered back fiercely, not wishing to attract the attention of the leopard. 'What do you mean, bringing me here? Are you *mad*? It could have got *me*!'

'There's nothing to worry about. Tell me: why do you think he went for that particular deer rather than the others?'

'How should I know? First one he caught up with, I suppose.'

'Right. It couldn't run as fast as the others; its legs weren't as strong or as long.'

'So?' I asked.

'It will never mate. It will never have young . . .'

'You don't say!' I exclaimed, mocking him. 'Of course, it won't. It's *dead*!'

'Right. Whereas the others – the ones lucky enough to be born with long, strong legs – they've got away. One day they'll mate.'

'Bully for them. Are you *sure* this is safe? What if that leopard starts looking for pudding?'

'Look, I've told you: you're OK. Trust me. As I was saying: they'll mate and have young. The young will take after their parents – in the same way as you're tall like your mother . . .'

Why bring *that* up? If he dares call me 'Beanpole' . . .

'But the deer that become parents aren't your average, run-of-the-mill deer; they're the faster ones – right? The slower ones got killed off – like that one out there. So, that means the young will be strong and fast like their parents. And when the strongest and fastest of *those* grow up and mate . . .'

'They'll have young that are even stronger and faster. Yes, I know.'

'Very good.'

'I do pay attention in class sometimes, you know. And that's how the animals came to be the way they are today, right?'

'That's what the theory says. Neat idea, eh?'

'But I thought *you* were supposed to have created the animals and made them the way they are,' I said. 'That's what it says in the Bible.'

'Sure, I created them,' he said. 'But that doesn't mean I have to sit down at the drawing board and design each one. Why not let it happen naturally? Some deer born faster than average, some slower – all a matter of chance. But what is *not* left to chance is the way the faster runners get selected out for mating. That's why it's called evolution by natural selection.'

Just then, a giant bird – I think it was an eagle – came swooping out of the sky. It landed on the ground and jabbed away with its beak at something. It was too far off for me to make out what it was attacking. But then it took off again. It had a twitching furry brown object in its claws. It mounted up into the air and made off for the top of a tall tree – heading for its nest, I suppose.

'Speed isn't everything,' the hacker said. 'Some animals have developed sharp claws or strong pointed beaks. Anything that gives them an advantage over their brothers and sisters will get selected out.'

'What's so special about human beings?' I asked. 'We don't run fast or have sharp claws . . .'

Whoosh!

The leopard had been quietly chewing away at the dead deer all this time. Suddenly, it shuddered and dropped to the ground. A spear stuck out of its neck. I looked around to see where it had come from.

Whoosh! Whoosh!

Spears flashed through the air, some hitting the leopard, others landing nearby. From behind some trees, came scruffy, long-haired men dressed in animal skins and furs – about half a dozen of them. They crept up to the leopard and prodded its body. It was dead. They started jabbering at each other and helping themselves to what was left of the deer.

'Your ancestors,' said the hacker. 'What's so special about humans you ask? Intelligence. (Though goodness knows, you'd hardly think it at times.) That's how your lot got to the top of the heap. Why have sharp claws when you can make spears, or bows and arrows? Much better.'

Just then, I noticed one of the hunters staring at me – right at me. I crouched down, heart pounding. Had he seen me? He had! Yelling something, he charged straight towards me, spear at the ready. OH, NO! I was about to be *unselected*, when . . .

Phew! My bedroom!

The picture had gone. It was like suddenly

coming out of a dream – a nightmare. One moment you're caught up in whatever you're dreaming about. The next, you're staring at your bedroom. It was a bit like that. Weird sensation it was. Like with that space trip yesterday. This time it was even more odd; like being beamed back in time. I don't mind telling you it took quite a while for my heart to stop thumping.

'So, that's the general idea,' said the hacker. 'You're descended from animals – from more primitive ones.'

'How far back does this evolution go?' I asked.

'To the bucket of slime. Not actually a bucket, of course. But slime, yes. It's called the "primordial soup". Evolution goes right back to non-living chemicals in the sea. Out of this sludge came very, very simple forms of life – so simple it would be hard to know whether to call them living or non-living – a bit like some bugs or viruses today.'

Viruses. A hacker would certainly know about *those*, I thought!

'But you must be able to tell the difference between something that's alive and something that's not,' I said.

'No. There's no real difference. It depends on what scientists decide to call "life".'

'But I thought scientists couldn't make life because . . . well . . . only you can make life. That's what Mum says.'

'A bottle of magic life-making potion up my

sleeve; I go around pouring a drop into this and a drop into that?'

'Something like that.'

'No need for that. There's nothing to stop life arising naturally, on its own. Evolution leads to more and more complicated things. Then one day, it reaches the level of the first living creature – no more than a tiny bug. This then develops into more advanced forms of life – ending up with humans. They start talking to each other. And that's important. They can now *share* their knowledge and understanding. It's then they start to think of more than just food and sex. They wonder whether there is anything beyond what they can see. Is there any meaning to life? That's when they begin to relate to me. And that's when things get interesting – because that's what it was all about – what it was all for.'

'How long did all this take – to go from chemicals to a human being?'

'4,500 million years,' he said.

'It only takes nine months now,' I suggested.

'Nine months?' the hacker asked. Then he started laughing – so loud I thought he'd be heard all over the house. 'True, very true. Now we've got the recipe . . .'

'OK,' I interrupted. 'So, if it's evolution, that proves what I was saying about the Bible. It proves that all the Adam and Eve stuff is rubbish . . .'

'Like *Neighbours*?'

'*Neighbours*? What do you mean? What's *Neighbours* got to do with it?'

'Well, that's rubbish too,' said the hacker.

'It's NOT!' I exclaimed. 'Everyone at school watches it. You ask.'

'But you don't think those people actually exist, do you?'

'Of course they don't. What's that got to do with it? It's a story.'

'Then, why isn't it rubbish?'

'Because it's a *good* story. It's very true to life. You learn a lot about yourself and what people are like from watching it.'

'Ah! So it *is* like Adam and Eve,' he said.

'What are you on about?'

'Well, the story of Adam and Eve doesn't have to be about real people for it to be true – *true to life*. The Biblical stories of Creation and of Adam and Eve are stories that help *you* to understand *yourself*. That's the point of them. They are stories about YOU. The name "Adam" isn't an ordinary name like "Sam" or "Paul" or "Lizzie". "Adam" means "Man" or "Humankind". Read these stories and they tell you about your relationship to the world, and to other people, and to me.'

'What sort of things?' I asked.

'Well, for a start, Adam was put in the Garden of Eden not just to have a good time, but to work hard at looking after it. In the same way, humans have been put on to the Earth to look after it. Not that you're making a very good job of it: dumping nuclear waste, poisoning the rivers and seas, creating acid rain, burning up the rain forests, destroying the ozone layer, wasting precious oil, gas and coal supplies . . .'

'Hey! It's not my fault! I'm only a kid,' I protested. 'I don't dump nuclear waste and all that. You tell the Prime Minister and all those people – the adults – those are the ones doing all these things.'

'Fair enough – as long as you don't find yourself doing the same things when it's your turn to make the decisions. Remember, there's nothing new about being Green. The Bible's been flogging that message for thousands of years – there in the Adam and Eve story. And that's not the only message in that story. It tells you that I made you in my own image.'

'What's that supposed to mean?' I asked.

'Well, you know how you take after your mum and dad in certain ways? You're tall like your mum . . .'

There he goes again. He must *know* it annoys me . . .

'You're impatient like your dad . . .'

What *is* this?

'Well, you also take after me. I'm a second kind of father to you. And because you're made like me the more you learn about me, the more you learn about yourself – your *true* self.'

'I am like *I AM . . .*' My voice trailed off. It sounded . . . well, strange.

'Exactly. Well done. That's another reason I'm called *I AM*. And what else? If I'm an extra sort of parent – a heavenly parent – you should listen carefully to any advice I give you.'

'Why? I don't need any help from you.'

'Because I want you to make the most of your life. I want you to be *really* happy . . .'

'And you have all the answers? You expect me to do whatever . . .'

'If only you would! No, there'll be times when you think you know best. You'll ignore me – go it alone. The Adam and Eve story has a lot to say about that – what happens when people disobey me.'

'If it's such a great idea obeying you, why don't people do it more often?' I asked.

'Evolution. If the evolution theory is right, you're an animal – with instincts. You have a tendency to be selfish, to want to do things your way. It's an instinct that evolved in your ancestors. It was part of their survival kit. It drove them to grab food and shelter for themselves and their families – killing if necessary. They couldn't afford to worry about the needs of others. If they hadn't developed that ruthless instinct they wouldn't have survived – and you wouldn't be here now. So it was lucky for you they had it. Trouble is that same instinct has now been passed on to you.'

'Me? Ruthless! Some hopes . . .'

'Oh, yes. The same selfish, self-seeking instinct. Not that you need it. There's no need to be selfish in order to stay alive today, but it's there all the same.'

I thought of Sooty and that bird. Instinct. That black snarling face, the bared teeth and the angry growling as we tried to get the bird out of her claws. It was a side of her I'd never seen before.

But then again, cats are just animals. Human beings are different – aren't they? Though come to think of it . . . *some* people behave like animals. Remember that time on the bus when those football supporters got on? A whole gang of them. It was all right at first. They were singing and laughing. Cheeking the conductor, but nothing serious; they paid their fares. They were all in a good mood. Their team had won. But then they spotted a couple walking along the pavement – wearing different scarves. Suddenly they all started shouting and swearing. They kept ringing the bell until the bus stopped. Then they all piled out and charged back down the street – just like a pack of wild animals. I wonder if those two got away.

'So I'm just an animal. Is that it?' I asked.

'That's what some people say. Others say you're just a pile of atoms – a machine. To some extent they're right. You might learn a lot about yourself by studying how other animals behave. And doctors, dentists, and surgeons often have to treat your body like a machine – one that's not working properly.'

'The dentist doing running repairs on worn-out teeth,' I suggested.

'That's right. But that's not to say there's no more to you than that.'

'What more is there?'

'That's where the Bible and other holy writings come in. They aren't putting forward rival theories to Darwin. Most religious people are quite happy to accept what scientists have to say about evolution.'

'They *do*!' I exclaimed.

'Certainly. No, what the Bible is saying is that as well as being an animal – as well as being a pile of chemicals – you're made in my image. It's saying that human beings have it in them to be God-like. If only they'd listen. Yes, if only . . . if only they would listen.'

He sounded sad. A sad God – I ask you!

'Enough of that,' he said, quickly pulling himself together. 'Next time . . . yes, next time we'll do something different. I know . . . I'll tell you a story! I take it you like stories? *I* love 'em!'

3   Not a Very Likely Story

'So what do you make of that, Inspector?' said this man pacing up and down the room with his hands behind his back.

'I'd never have thought it,' replied the policeman.

'Nothing to it really. You see, our sweet little Miss Pringle overlooked something – a vital clue – the ashtray.'

'The ashtray? What about the ashtray?'

'It was full. It was full but she didn't smoke. And another thing. The gun. How come she knew where to find it under the cushion? Do you really think she came across that by accident?'

'Come to think of it, that did seem a bit of a coincidence – her rearranging the cushion like that, and just happening to come across it. Yes. Yes, by Jove, it's all beginning to make sense.'

Something was wrong. I had typed *I AM* as before, but instead of getting through to the hacker, the computer seemed to be picking up one of the normal broadcasts – one of the TV channels.

But don't you need an aerial for that? I asked myself. Perhaps it has a built-in one. That must be it. As for the film, I half remember seeing it before.

I pressed the 'Escape' key and got the Menu back.. I reckoned I must have pressed the wrong keys the first time. Very carefully I typed *I AM*, determined not to make any mistake . . .

'Hi, there! What's the matter? Didn't you like it?' asked the hacker.

Ah! That's better.

'That was you? I thought I'd got BBC or ITV by mistake,' I said.

'Of course it was me. Thought you'd enjoy it. I love whodunits.'

'I've seen it. It was lousy.'

'Oh? What was wrong with it?'

'Too far-fetched. All those coincidences. It's the one where the bullet goes through his body, bounces off the mantelpiece and into the grand-father clock and stops the clock so the detective knows the time of the murder. Oh yes, and there was that postman – the postman who just hap-pened to be the exact double of the man who got shot – so that's why you're left thinking he's not really dead until the end. Stupid. It all worked out too neatly. It never happens in real life like that.'

'You could tell?' said the hacker.

'Of course.'

'Oh.'

There was a pause.

'Why? What's the matter?' I asked.

'Nothing. No, it's nothing . . .' he said thoughtfully.

I waited.

'Actually . . .' he began again.

'Yes?'

'No, I can't really ask you . . .'

'Go on,' I said impatiently. 'What is it?'

'Well, I was wondering whether you'd do me a favour. You see, I've written a whodunit myself.'

'*You* have?'

'Yes. The story of how I made you.'

'Evolution? We've done that,' I said.

'Partly evolution, but mainly all that happened before evolution got started – before there was an Earth. The story of the World from the very beginning.'

'I don't know anything about *that*,' I said. 'What favour?'

'Well, seeing as how you seem to know whether stories are true-to-life or not . . . I wondered if you'd care to hear this one. You could tell me what you think of it. Is it too far-fetched to be real? Is it obvious that it's been made-up, rather than happened naturally? That sort of thing.'

'Well . . . if it's not too long.'

'It's a bit long – 15,000 million years long. But I'll give you the shortened version, OK? Here goes . . .'

BANG! The computer blew up! I reeled back, almost falling off my chair with fright.

No. Wait. It seems to be all right. For one horrible moment . . .

'What . . . what was THAT?' I stammered.

'That? That's how it starts. My story. The Big Bang. The creation of the Universe.'

It was a good thing my parents were out. So was Lizzie – it was Friday and she was at the club.

'A bang?' I asked. 'It all started with a bang?'

'That's right.'

'What's that got to do with six days?'

'Six days?' he asked.

'That's what Lizzie says. It's in the Bible, isn't it? You should know. It says you created the world in six days. I don't remember anything about a bang.'

'Ah, but that's another of those ancient stories. You don't have to take it as literally true.'

'There you go again,' I said in disgust. 'The Bible gets caught out and you say, "Ah, but it doesn't mean . . ."'

'Well, I can't help it. That's the way it is. After all, when you talk about the Creation story, which one do you mean?'

'Which . . .? I mean the one in the Bible,' I said.

'But there are two: one in the first chapter of the Bible, the other – a completely different one –

in Chapter Two. The two stories contradict each other – that's if you insist on treating them as scientific theories of what actually happened.'

'So . . . people were ignorant in those days.'

'That's not kind. Didn't know when two stories contradicted each other? They might not have known much science, but that's not to say they weren't *intelligent*.'

'Well, if they were so clever, why the two stories?'

'Because of their deep-down messages. Like the deep-down messages in the Adam and Eve story. That's what creation stories are about. They're not about *science*.'

'What messages?' I asked.

'Well, for a start that there is just one God – me. You've no idea how long it took to work that one out. Originally they thought there were lots of gods. And what else? Yes. The fact that I made everything – I created it all, and that the world is good.'

'It's nothing of the kind! Earthquakes, famines, pain, and all that. It's horrible, if you ask me.'

'Try telling that to a drowning man. There's nothing like the thought of dying to make people realize that it's worth fighting to stay alive,' he said. 'Anyway, where were we? The Big Bang. All the matter flying apart.'

'The galaxies?'

'No. There weren't any galaxies to begin with;

34

just gas – white hot gas. That's what came out of
the Bang.'

I looked hard at the screen . . .

Sure enough, whiteness was all I could see.

'In time this gas cooled down,' he continued.

As he spoke, the light dimmed. It was then I
began to make out these swirling masses of gas,
spreading outwards, stretching further and
further outwards, as far as the eye could see.
Gradually it began to break up. Clumps or
clouds started to form. Each of these sucked in
the gas nearby and became more and more
dense. After a while there were just these separ-
ate clouds with dark empty space in between. I
was just outside one of them and seemed to be
travelling along with it. The others were now a
long way off, and were steadily disappearing
still further into the distance. In the end they
were no more than tiny faint smudges in the sky.

As for the cloud alongside me, it had now
flattened out into a disc shape. It was slowly
rotating, rather like a record on a turntable. Not
only that, but things had started to happen in the
disc itself. Small eddies or whirlpools were
beginning to form – rather like the swirl you get
around the plug hole when the water runs out of
the bath. Then something remarkable happened. As each of these eddies became smaller
and denser, it began to glow brightly – ever so
brightly. It looked as though these little balls of

gas had caught fire. It was quite wonderful. It was as though someone had switched on the Christmas illuminations. The disc became alight with thousands, millions of these tiny points of light. It was . . . it was the Galaxy! I recognized it. Suddenly I realized what those 'tiny points of light' really were.

'Stars!' I exclaimed excitedly.

'Right,' said the hacker. 'That's how the stars formed. Magic, eh?'

'And the Earth?' I asked.

'No, no. You're going too fast. There aren't any planets yet. You need rocky materials for that, and there aren't any yet – only very light gases. That's all that came out of the Big Bang – not the bigger atoms I need to make planets and humans.'

'So, what's the difficulty? If you're God, you can do anything you want.'

'Sure. I could create different kinds of atoms. Abracadabra – just like that! Miracles? No problem. But why not let it happen naturally? That's what I say. Anyway, I had this brilliant idea. To make bigger atomic particles out of the smaller ones I needed the particles to melt a bit so they could glue to each other. So, where could I find an oven to cook them in? Exactly. The stars! In the middle of stars, atomic particles are continually bumping into each other, and because it's so hot, they stick. So, that was it. Easy, yes? Easy, no! Big, big problems. Carbon's the headache. Your body needs carbon. But making it is tricky. It could be done, just – by fiddling.'

'What do you mean, "fiddling"?'

'The forces of nature – how strong they are – gravity and that sort of thing. Most of the time it doesn't matter too much how strong the forces are. But when it comes to making carbon . . . To make carbon you've got to get three small particles of a light gas to stick together at about the same time – and that spells big trouble. You can't do it – not unless the forces are just right. Make the sticky forces a bit too strong or a bit too weak: no carbon. They had to be fixed absolutely spot on. And that's the problem. Any scientist looking at the forces today knows it must be a set-up job. Either that or it is a really way-out coincidence – far worse than anything you saw in that detective film . . .'

'This can't be right,' I said. 'You say all this happens inside stars – the particles sticking together to make carbon and other stuff?'

'Yes.'

'And that's the stuff that makes up my body and the Earth, right?'

'Yes. What's the problem?' he asked.

'But I'm not in the middle of a star. Neither is the Earth.'

'Dead right. That brings us to the next hurdle: how to get the wretched stuff out of the star. More fiddling the books I'm afraid.'

All the time we had been speaking, we had

drifted closer and closer to the Galaxy. By now we had begun to enter it. We passed one star after another until they were all around us. Suddenly, without warning, one of them close by – a particularly large one – flared up with incredible brightness. When the glare died down, the star had gone! In its place was a cloud of gas billowing outwards from where the star had originally been.

'Ah!' exclaimed the hacker. 'That's what I was about to describe. I had to fix things so that stars above a certain size would explode. Sounds unlikely, gravity being strong and holding everything together. But eventually I figured out a way of getting them to explode and throw the carbon and other stuff out.'

As I continued to watch, some of the gas from the exploded star developed a whirlpool. As this became smaller and denser it began to glow. Another star – a smaller one this time. Not only that but I noticed several tiny whirlpools had developed outside this main one. As these became smaller and denser they did not glow like the star did. Instead they became round dark balls; I could see them only by the light they reflected from the new star. As we drifted in closer to them, I noticed that one of these balls was blue with white streaks! The Earth! I had witnessed the birth of the Earth – and of the Sun and the other planets.

'OK,' said God. 'That's got the Earth. Now I

can start making you out of the raw materials on the surface of the Earth.'

'By evolution?' I suggested.

'Yes. This is where evolution takes over.'

'And how long did all this take – from the Big Bang?' I asked.

'A long time. From the Big Bang to the formation of the Earth, 10,000 million years; then a further 4,500 million years of evolution to get to humans. Which brings me to yet another problem,' he added wearily. 'All the time evolution was going on, I needed to have the Sun burning – to supply the energy. Have you any idea how difficult that was? It's those wretched forces again. It turns out that it's almost impossible to fix them so stars will be hot enough to catch fire, but then not *too* hot that they burn themselves out before evolution has done its job. What a juggling act!'

'So you're saying that for all those millions of years you had to keep on changing the forces of nature . . .'

'No, no. Sorry. That's just my way of talking. No. I'm God. I have this knack of seeing the future. I don't have to have second thoughts about anything. What I've been talking about is how I came to choose the forces in the *first* place. What I'm saying is that there is only a tiny, tiny selection of forces that will produce life.'

'So?'

'So, if there's a universe with life in it – like this

one – it's obvious someone has deliberately designed it for that purpose. It's too far-fetched to have happened naturally. The odds against are astronomical – literally.'

'How astronomical?' I asked.

'Hard to put a figure on it. Millions to one against. Squillions to one. The whole story looks as phoney as that detective story I showed you. So, what do you think?'

Clever. You have to hand it to this hacker. If I admit that, by looking at the world and how it operates, I can tell it's all been deliberately set up to produce life – that would be the same as saying there must be *someone* behind it. In other words – God.

'You're trying to force me into accepting that you exist . . .'

'No, no. That's not it at all. No, I would hate anyone to use what I've been telling you as an *argument* – an argument to try and *make* someone, against their will, accept that I exist. A set of little clues – to those who already know me – to let them see how things are working out nicely according to plan? Fine. But I do seem to have overdone it. Now that these coincidences have come to light, even those who have always said I don't exist, are beginning to talk of "Him who fixed it".'

'So, is there any other way of explaining them?' I asked.

'An infinite number of universes.'

'What?'

'Yes. An infinite number . . . it's an idea some scientists have come up with. They suggest that instead of just one universe, there might be lots of them, all running on different lines. In some of these universes, everything is just right for producing intelligent life; in others – the vast, vast majority of them – it's not. You're a living creature; you must find yourself in one of the first type. (You obviously couldn't find yourself in the second.) That way there's no mystery. Your universe is not a very likely one, but there are so many attempts at different kinds of universe, yours is bound to come up in the end. That way no one has to fiddle anything; you can just put it down to chance.'

'And that's the scientific explanation of what's going on?' I said.

'No. Sorry. It's an idea that happens to have been put forward by a few scientists – but there's nothing scientific about it. These other universes – if they exist – don't have anything to do with each other. You can never do an experiment to prove that they're there. It's all just one big guess. That's not science. In science you check out your ideas. Besides, there's another thing about science: it explains things simply using just a few basic ideas. You could hardly come up with anything more complicated and over-the-top than an infinite number of universes all working on different lines! So it's not science.'

'But there's nothing to stop people believing in it.'

'True. Some think it's more reasonable to believe in that than in me. Can't think why,' he added.

'You designed the Universe to bring human beings into existence, right? That's what you're telling me,' I said. 'But why? What's so special about human beings?'

'I wanted someone to *love*,' he replied. 'I wanted someone to love me. I wanted someone to share with me the joy of simply *being*. It's as simple as that really.'

'In that case – if the Universe is just meant to be our home – you rather overdid it, didn't you? I mean, how *big* is it?'

'Big enough – but only just. Given that it starts with a Big Bang, it has to keep flying apart for all the time it takes for intelligent life to develop. I couldn't have gravity pulling everything back together again before humans had had a chance to appear. So, work it out: the matter in the Universe flying apart for about 15,000 million years at over 100,000 miles per second – that ends up BIG. Mind you, in talking about human beings, I don't just mean you lot on Earth. There are plenty of other forms of life in other parts of the Universe just as advanced as you are. Most don't look at all human, but I'm just as interested in them as in you. The Universe is for them too.'

'And what if I don't go along with all this?

43

What if I don't think the Universe was designed to bring me into existence? What if it's not all about loving you, and you loving us, and all that? What then?'

'In that case, you're a nothing-type thing, lost in an infinity of universes. There's no reason for you being here; you just happened, and when you die you will unhappen.'

Sounded pretty bleak. But I shrugged my shoulders: 'OK. If that's the way it is,' I said, 'that's the way it is. I'd rather face up to that than kid myself with a cosy fairy story.'

'And as I have said before, that's fair enough. That's an honest reply. Feeling the way you do, that is the kind of reply I would want from you. Besides, it's not all bad. After all, suppose for a minute you did believe in me; what then? You'd have to accept that you owed everything to me, and that I made you for a purpose. That would mean your life was not your own; you ought to lead it the way *I* want you to. And that might sometimes not be the way you wish. In fact, there could be times when the going gets real rough. So, I suggest you go easy with all that talk about it being "cosy". Indeed, if we look at things from your point of view, you owe nobody anything; life is just an accident; you're free to do whatever you like with it. Now *that's* what *I* call "cosy"! So cosy, I'm surprised anyone ever picks *me*!'

4 Miracles or Packed Lunches

I made a brilliant discovery today! Well, it was
Premikar and me. She's my friend. We do
science projects together. We had to put
weights in a pan and hang the pan by a piece of
string. We then had to let the pan swing from
side to side, like a pendulum, and see how long
it took for ten swings, using a stop watch. Got
into a right muddle, we did. We tried changing
the weights and the length of the string. Took
lots of readings; couldn't make any sense of
them. But then Miss Francis said we should
change one thing at a time. Keep the length of
the string the same; start the swing from the
same point every time; find out what happens
when you change only the weights. It's then we
made our big discovery. You'll never guess
what it was. You'd think the heavier the
weights, the longer the time of the swing, right?
Wrong! It didn't matter what weight was in the
pan; the time was always the same! Amazing!
Miss Francis says that's why pendulums were
used in clocks (before they had digital watches).
The time of the swing only depends on the

length of the string, she said. We're going to check that out next Thursday.

Miss Francis has been telling us about the laws of nature. Nothing to do with ordinary laws – getting nicked for stealing or doing someone in. No, these are rules that tell nature what it has to do. Everything's done according to rules. Doesn't look like it at first – like with the pendulum – but when you look at nature very carefully, in a scientific way, it all makes sense. Anyway, that's what she says.

All this talk about the laws gave me an idea: proof that the hacker wasn't God. Couldn't wait to get home and tell him . . .

'Hello, Sam. Had a good day?' said the hacker when I got through.

'Yes, thank you. A very good day,' I replied. 'Yes, we've been doing science today.'

'Excellent! I like people learning about my world. What in particular?'

'Pendulums, and the way the time of the swing doesn't depend on the weight . . .'

'Ha! That one. Neat trick, eh? Fools everyone.'

'Look, cut it out, will you. I *know* you're a hacker – I know you can't be God.'

'Oh, how's that?' he asked.

'Simple, really. If you were God you would be interfering with the workings of this computer, wouldn't you? You'd be stopping it from doing what it would normally do – so as to get your messages in, right?'

'Er, yes. So?'

'Well that would be a miracle, right? You'd be mucking around with nature. A scientist watching what was going on in the computer would see that the laws of nature weren't being obeyed. And that's silly. It's not possible. Scientists have proved that miracles can't happen.'

'They've what! Good heavens, when did they do that? No one tells me anything.'

'*Everyone* knows that. Miracles are out. Nature's run by laws.'

'Well, yes – most of the time. I should know; they're *my* laws. So, what's the problem? You make a discovery: the time of the swing doesn't depend on the weights. Now you expect it won't *ever* depend on the weights. Not a bad guess – not bad at all. But you can't be *sure*. Some day I might have some special reason for wanting something different.'

'So? I often want things to be different. That's not to say I do a miracle. And if *I* can't do them, why should you?'

'Oh, come now! I've already told you: they're *my* laws. I can do what I like with them.'

'OK, if you're so clever, do a miracle now. Right now. Come on . . .' I thought for a moment. 'I know. Make it rain. Yes, that's it. It hasn't rained all day, and . . . hold on.' I checked out of the window. The stars were shining brightly; not a cloud to be seen. 'Yes,' I said, 'make it rain – and I'll believe you.'

'The number of times . . . ' he muttered to himself. 'Look, let's get one thing clear: party tricks are out. Not my style.'

'That's a cop-out.'

'Can't help that. I'm not doing one.'

'Why not?' I challenged.

'What's the point? OK, I make it rain. What then? Do you believe I exist? Of course not. You think there must have been a cloud you hadn't noticed. Even if you did believe, so what? Our friendship gets off on the wrong foot. You'd always be expecting me to do miracles for you – rain today, a million pounds tomorrow. Or if I did something really spectacular, you might be frightened of me, and I certainly don't want that. I want people to love me – for my own sake – the way I love them. *Forcing* people to believe in me would be a waste of time.'

'So when *do* you do miracles?'

'I might do a miracle for someone who really needs it – and who already believes in me. Yes, that's when I like doing them.'

'What about the miracles in the Bible? Did you do those?'

'Does it matter?'

'Of course it matters! If you didn't – the Bible's lying.'

'Lying? That's a bit strong. It all depends.'

'On what?' I demanded crossly.

'Depends on what the Bible was getting at –
what the miracle stories were *really* about.
Which one do you have in mind?'

I didn't know what to say. I hardly ever read
the Bible.

'How about this one?' suggested the hacker,
and the screen came to life . . .

A large crowd – people dressed in long robes
and head-scarves, jostling about on a sea-shore.
There were boats bobbing up and down in the
background. People were pouring off them to
join us on the beach.

'You said he did *what*?' asked a man at my
elbow.

'I've told you,' said a woman. 'The lad had
five small loaves and a couple of fish. That's all.
And yet we all had plenty to eat – and there was
lots left over.'

'Well, you couldn't have been very hungry.'

'Starving. We were all starving. The kids
were crying. We'd been with him all day, and
we were miles from any shops or cafés. Then
suddenly there's all this food.'

'And how many did you say there were?'

'Thousands. Yes, must have been. Thousands.'

'Get away!'

'It's true. Ask anyone. A real miracle it was.'

'You know what I think? I reckon you took
packed lunches . . .'

'Packed lunches!'

'Yes. No one let on because this Jesus fellow would have made you share the food out – with the others who hadn't brought any. But this kid shared his with Jesus, you all felt guilty, and owned up.'

'There were people standing right next to Jesus at the time, if you must know. They say it wasn't like that at all.'

'Oh, people forget. They don't really remember things properly.'

'We're talking about *yesterday*! Anyway, see for yourself!'

'Can't wait. It's the end of the month. I could do with a handout,' he laughed.

As he said that, the crowd nearby parted. A man stepped forward. Nothing to look at – short, with dark hair. But all eyes were on him. I could see people nudging each other and nodding in his direction. They stopped talking. He came up to us – right up to us – I could have reached out and touched him.

'Is that the only reason you're here – a free lunch?' he said to the man beside me – the one who had been arguing.

The man mumbled something I didn't catch.

'People think too much about food,' said Jesus – at least I assumed this *was* Jesus. 'Not much point to it really. Eat a meal today – by tomorrow you're hungry again. Why look to me for that kind of food, when I have food from God? With my sort of food you won't ever be hungry again.'

The crowd started murmuring: 'Never be hungry!' 'I told you he was mental.' 'Where is this food?'

Jesus smiled. He pointed to himself, and said, '*I* am the bread of life.'

At that, everything started to go misty. A sea fog had started to drift in. Either that or my eyes were going funny. I blinked . . .

I sat there staring at the screen as the picture faded.

Is that *it*, I wondered. What now?

'Mr Hacker – God?' I asked. 'Are you still there?'

'Yes. So. What did you make of it?'

'Make of it? Nothing. I was there the wrong day. It was all over – the food business happened the day before.'

'Yes, I know that. But so what? Miracle or packed lunches? The important thing was what Jesus said afterwards – the next day. What did you make of *that*?'

'Nothing. He didn't say anything.'

'But he told you about the bread of life.'

'Yes, I know that. But what's that supposed to mean? How can someone be *bread*? Who does he think we are? Cannibals!'

'He didn't mean *ordinary* bread. Sure, he was talking about hunger – but not ordinary hunger. A different sort – a deep-down kind of hunger – a hunger that drives people to look for meaning and purpose in life.'

'I'm not looking for meaning and purpose. I *know* what I'm going to do with my life.' I paused for a moment to think. 'Yes, at present I'm working for my exams. Then, when I grow up, I shall lead a group – like Jan in *Desert Mirage* – that's them in the poster above the bed. After that I'm going into films; get loads of money; be famous; get married – happily,' I said, thinking of Mum and Dad's recent rows. 'I'll have kids who'll think the world of me, and . . . yes, I'll live in a huge house, and go everywhere by taxi – and live until I'm ninety.'

'Really? I mean . . . are you sure? I can't remember having you down for all that,' said the hacker. 'Anyway, suppose you did have all that . . . would that make you happy – *really* happy?'

'Happy? Over the Moon! Isn't that what everybody wants?'

'Everybody might want it but that doesn't mean to say they're *right* in wanting it. How many rich and famous people are happy? The more you get of those sorts of thing, the more you want. They're like drugs. You wait and see.'

'Yes, I'll wait and see,' I said. 'Anyway. What do *you* reckon makes people happy if it's not money and stuff?'

'True happiness? That comes from following the example of people like Jesus. Living a much simpler life – loving people – doing the right thing. Happiness sneaks up on you when you least expect it – like when you're doing something for someone else, unselfishly. It comes from giving rather than getting; forgiving people rather than getting your own back on them.'

'I still think passing exams and having lots of money would make me pretty happy.'

'Give it time.'

'Anyway, what's this got to do with bread?' I asked.

'Well, as I was saying, people get this deep-down type of hunger. What should you do about it? It helps to have a picture – a mental picture. You think of Jesus feeding people's ordinary hunger. That then reminds you that Jesus also has the answer to the more important deep-down kind of hunger – the kind you're going to have when you're being driven around in your taxi wondering, "Is this *it*?"'

'But did he, or did he not, feed thousands of people on . . . however many loaves and fishes it was? I just don't believe it.'

There was a pause before the hacker spoke again.

'Look, Sam,' he said eventually, 'I don't think you're quite getting the right idea about all this science you're learning. Don't get me wrong,' he added hastily. 'I'm all for people learning as much science as they can. But it's very limited.

It tackles only certain kinds of question – and not necessarily the most important questions. You mustn't lose sight of that. Even with the things it does talk about – matter, space, and time – even there . . . Oh, I don't know. Somehow scientific ways of talking never seem to capture their mystery. Especially the mystery they have when I touch them in a special way.' He sighed.

'But, then again,' he continued, 'if you don't believe in miracles – for the present at least – there's nothing you can do about it. You can't *force* yourself to believe. No, if you don't believe, I suggest you try to concentrate instead on what these stories have to say about *you*.'

Another picture came up on the screen . . .

This time we were in a narrow dusty street. Jesus and some others were coming towards me. But before they reached me they stopped next to a beggar sitting in a doorway. He was blind; you could tell from his closed sunken eyes. Jesus stood there chatting with his friends. They were talking about the beggar. Then Jesus crouched down beside him, and started spitting! I'm not kidding; spitting on the ground. My mum would have told him off. She says it's rude to spit – unless you're cleaning your teeth. Anyway, that's what he did. In fact, he did it several times – spitting on the same spot. He then rubbed his finger in this mud and then – you won't believe this – he smeared the muck over the man's eyes!

I couldn't believe it. I was about to yell at him to stop, when I noticed a funny thing: the blind man didn't seem to mind! It was almost as though he had been expecting something like that to happen. Next, I heard Jesus tell the man to go and wash. Well, he needed to after that! The man got up and went off down the street.

Next minute he was back – running and shouting at the top of his voice. He could see! He rushed passed me. I could see his eyes. They were wide open and shiny. Immediately a crowd gathered and the arguments began.

A man went over to Jesus and asked him straight who he was. Jesus replied. 'I am the light of the world. I have come into this world, so that those without sight may see, and those who think they see turn blind.'

As he said that last bit, he glanced across at a group that had gathered on the other side of the road. Important-looking people they were. They'd been eyeing him for some time. One called out, 'You'd better not be talking about us. Because if you are . . .'

'Blind? If you *knew* you were blind you would not be guilty, but since you say you see, then you are guilty.'

'O-oh,' someone murmured. 'Looks like trouble again . . .'

A fight was about to break out. But – just as it was getting interesting . . .

The picture faded.

'So?' I demanded. 'What was *that* supposed to be about?'

'Blindness,' replied the hacker. 'Different kinds of blindness. There are people – like those Jesus was talking to at the end – who *think* they see their way ahead clearly. They think they know what they should be doing with their life. But they don't; they're blind – as blind in their own way as that beggar was.'

'And you're saying Jesus has the answer?'

'Exactly. He has the answer to this deep-down kind of blindness, just as he has the answer to deep-down hunger.'

'But him curing the blind man – that doesn't have to be a miracle,' I said. 'Doctors are able to cure all sorts of diseases now. Jesus was just ahead of his time. He was a really good doctor.'

'Possibly. If that's what you want to think. But again, the important thing is what these miracle stories have to say about *you* – you as you are *today*.'

'It's got nothing to do with me,' I said.

'It has *everything* to do with you, Sam. You're blind . . .'

'Blind! ME?' I protested.

'Yes. Deep-down blind. You're dazzled by all these thoughts of fame, and riches, and success. You don't see them for what they are. When you do – when you begin to see the way ahead more clearly – then you will no longer be deep-down blind. It's then you will start to want something else in your life – that's what the deep-down hunger was all about. It will then be time to do something about *that*.'

This is getting dead boring, I thought.

'I don't know about all this,' I said. 'If the Bible's got something to say, why doesn't it come straight out with it? All this talk of miracles that might or might not have happened . . .'

'One more thing,' said the hacker. 'Did you notice anything odd about some of the things Jesus said?'

'No.'

'Well, did you notice how he said, "I am the bread of life"? And "I am the light of the world"? Jesus uses those words "*I am*" a lot. Odd, don't you think? Remind me to tell you about it sometime.'

5   Seeing is Believing – Perhaps

I was beginning to enjoy these arguments with the hacker. It's not that we agreed on much, but I liked the way he *listened* to me. He seemed really interested in what I had to say. Made a nice change. But one thing annoyed me more and more: he knew me, but I still didn't know who he was. I decided to have it out with him.

'Look,' I said. 'If you're really God then I want to see you – face to face. I want you right here in this room.'

'Oh. Why's that?' came the reply.

'Stop playing the innocent. You know perfectly well why. Seeing is believing – that's why.'

That's stumped you, Mr Hacker.

But then I felt uneasy. Suppose he *was* God. Suppose he *did* suddenly appear. What then?

'Do you believe in radio waves?' he said all of a sudden.

Now, I ask you: what's that got to do with anything?

'Of course I believe in radio waves,' I replied. 'That's got nothing . . .'

'Ever seen them?' he asked.

'Radio waves? Er . . . no. But I don't have to.'

'Why not?'

'*Everybody* knows there are radio waves. You wouldn't get anything on the radio without them, would you?'

'But you don't *see* the radio waves – not the waves themselves.'

'No. But I don't have to,' I said. 'I can prove they're there by switching on the radio.'

'So, what are you saying? You know they're there because of what they *do* – not because you *see* them?'

'Er . . . well, yes. Yes, that's right. They *do* things.'

'So why insist on seeing me?' he asked.

'Because you don't do *anything*.'

'But I do lots of things.'

'Name one,' I challenged.

'It's difficult to know where to start.'

'Too right!'

Ignoring me, he continued, 'I sort of . . . well . . . I sort of do *everything*. I've told you that before. I'm responsible for everything that exists.'

'That sounds awfully important,' I said, sarcastically. 'But what does that *mean*? What do you actually *do*? Point to something. It's not like radio waves: no radio waves – no programme on the radio. That's science for you. But there's nothing in science books to say I have to believe in you to explain anything.'

'You've got me there,' he admitted. 'No, I'm not that sort of an explanation.' He paused. 'How can I put it? Yes, I suppose I'd have to say it was more a case of . . . well, *sensing* my presence. Yes, sensing my presence behind everything.'

'What's that supposed to mean?' I asked suspiciously.

'Sensing my presence? Well . . . take a look out of the window. Go on, Sam. Have a look.'

The Moon was coming up, very thin and curved. Then gradually, as my eyes got used to the darkness, away from the brightness of the screen, I began to make out the stars. I recognized the Plough. It's the only one I'm sure about.

'Beautiful, isn't it?' he said. 'It's on nights like these people feel my presence behind it all. You do too – don't you? Just a little?'

'No,' I said firmly. 'I do not.'

'Oh. That's a shame. Lots of people do.'

'How?'

'Oh, come now. Don't tell me you've *never* sensed the presence of someone you couldn't see.'

I thought for a moment. Then I remembered something. It happened on holiday. We'd been staying on a farm and I was walking down the lane at night. It was pitch black. I wasn't used to that. Absolutely black it was. No street lights or anything. I was stumbling along this lane.

Couldn't see where I was going. I got frightened. *Someone was watching me out of the dark.* At least that's what it felt like. He was silently keeping pace with me on the other side of the hedge, waiting for a gap through which he could pounce. When I stopped, he stopped; when I went on, he went on. I've never been so scared. No reason for it. I just felt it. Boy, was I relieved to get round the corner and see the lights of the farmhouse windows.

'Yes,' I said cautiously. 'It did happen once – but it was only imagination. That's all it ever is.'

'Maybe. Maybe not. Many people think that on a starlit night I reveal to them something of my power and majesty.'

I turned back to the computer. The hacker had brought up a picture. It showed a snowflake. I recognized it from photographs I once saw in a book. When I say I recognized it, I don't mean I recognized that particular one. They're all supposed to be different – I think. Anyway, there are lots of different patterns, but all very beautiful.

'A nice eye for beauty and detail, don't you think?' he said. 'And how about this?'

The snowflake disappeared and we were in a garden. It was lovely. Masses and masses of flowers.

'The world didn't have to be this beautiful, you know. It's the way it is because that's how I am. There are people who feel especially close

to me in a garden. Again, I am letting them sense my presence. The beauty of nature . . . music . . . poetry. They all help people to respond to me. And how about these . . .'

$$F = ma; v = u + ft; E = mc^2$$

The screen was filled with scientific equations!

'When you first look at what goes on in the world, it seems a mad jumble – like when you first started playing around with that pendulum the other day. But then you look closer, and it's not like that. Behind the scenes there are just a few simple rules operating – a few laws of nature controlling everything. Of course, it takes a bit of intelligence to work it out, but it does all make sense.'

'So?'

'Well, if it takes intelligence to work it out, might it not have taken intelligence to set it up in the first place? Study science and you learn something about the way my mind works.'

'Rubbish. Scientists don't believe in you,' I said.

'*Some* scientists don't believe in me. But so what? The same is true of any kind of job. Some believe, some don't. Plenty of scientists believe in me.'

'Well, I don't know. Just because the laws make sense doesn't mean *you* have to be behind it all. Nor behind the stars, and gardens, and stuff. They're just *things*. That's all we're looking at: things and what things do.'

For quite some time, nothing happened. But then on the screen came some writing . . .

'*A QUIZ. Which of the following has a mind (i.e. which of them can experience feelings of pain, love, anger, fear, etc?) Answer yes or no for each.*'

A quiz? What's he up to now?

Football. The screen showed a footballer crashing to the ground. He rolled over and over, clutching his shin. The referee ran towards the penalty spot, pointing. The picture closed in on the player's face. It was screwed up in agony. The caption said '*Y/N*'.

I don't get it. Yes or No? Does the footballer have a *mind*? Is that what he's asking? How stupid! Of course he's got a mind. He's a *man*, isn't he? He's in pain. What a waste of time.

I pressed the *Y* key.

Secondly, a cat, mewing. A blizzard was blowing. The poor, snow-covered little thing looked frozen.

Again I pressed *Y*.

Then a worm. It was slowly crawling over the ground. Suddenly, CLUNK! A garden spade came down and sliced through it. Ugh! The worm writhed about. I quickly pressed *Y* once more.

Next, an excerpt from a TV programme about flower arrangement. The end of the flower's stem was being bashed. It was then put in a vase. I remembered Mum showing me how bashing helped the flowers take up water better. The picture closed in on the flower.

Flowers having minds? Shouldn't have thought so.

This time I chose N.

Then came a film showing a waterfall. I waited.

Is that *it*? A waterfall? A waterfall having a *mind*?

I pressed N.

Finally, a brick. Yes, a brick! Again I picked N.

'That was interesting,' said the hacker.

What's interesting about *that*, I wondered.

'No problem over the human being and the cat having minds,' he continued. 'Nor about the waterfall and the brick having none. The flower? Flowers are alive, remember. Some people talk to flowers . . .'

'Flowers have feelings?'

'Some people believe they do. Let's hope they don't – I wouldn't want to have my feet crushed like that – assuming I had feet. And how about that worm? You said yes to that one. Why?'

'Obvious. It was cut in two; it was in pain.'

'Both halves?' he asked.

'What do you mean?'

'Both halves of the worm were twisting about. Are you saying both halves were in pain?

Did its mind split into two, or what? Ever thought that it might not have a mind at all? Could be that its body twists about like that simply because of contractions in muscle tissue caused by electrical currents and chemical changes.'

He's right: both halves *were* writhing about. *Two* minds? Surely not . . .

I sat there thinking. I suppose it's the same with fish. That day I went fishing with Dad – the *one* day I went. He's always fishing at weekends. He kept on badgering me to go with him. I did this time. Talk about boring. Never again. I hated it when the fish got caught. Fancy having a jagged hook stuck in the roof of your mouth. I told him I thought it was horrible, but he said the fish didn't feel pain. How did he know? It must be the same with worms. You can't really be sure one way or the other, I suppose.

'So? What's the answer?' I asked. 'Does the worm feel anything? And what about fish?'

'I'm afraid I can't tell you that. Well, it would spoil everybody's fun thinking about these questions if I told you the answers.'

'Huh! So that was a right waste of time.'

'I wouldn't say that. After all, why was it difficult to decide which of these had a mind? In every case – human being, cat, worm, flower, waterfall, brick – in every one of them, all you had to work on were outward physical appearances.

That's all. You were looking at *things*. What it looked like – how it behaved. No direct contact mind-to-mind. Even with the footballer, you could only *assume* from his behaviour that he was in pain. You know that when you bang your own shin, you behave like that, and it hurts. So you assumed the same was true for him. But you can't be sure. You can't check it out by feeling *his* pain.'

Actually, it did occur to me the footballer might not have been in pain at all. It happened in the penalty area, and he was making a right meal of it. He could have been faking it. But even so, that's no reason to say he didn't have a mind!

'This is silly. All human beings have minds. It's obvious.'

'No, it's not,' he said. 'All you *know* – all you can be *certain* about – is that *you* have a mind. Just YOU. That's all you directly experience. Of course, you also know that your mind has something to do with your physical body. When something physical happens to your body (say, you bang your shin), then something happens mentally (you feel a pain). So, when you see other physical bodies, and they look very much like your own, you assume – but only *assume* – that they have minds too. Bang their shins, and their minds will feel pain.'

'Well, what's wrong with that?' I asked. 'In any case, it's not just that. Other people *tell* me they feel pain.'

'True. Other bodies speak about pains going on in their minds and why shouldn't you believe them? But you have to take their word for it. That's all I'm saying.'

'So it *is* OK to believe other people have minds?'

'Of course,' he said. 'It would be crazy not to. Why should you be the only thinking, feeling person in the world?'

'So that's all right then. What about animals?' I asked.

'Ah well, this is where it gets interesting. Now we're dealing with things that are *not* copies of your own body. Some are close – apes and monkeys – some not so close – cats. Then there are worms, and so on down to germs and viruses, plants, and bricks. How closely alike to a human body do these things have to be in order for them to have minds – in order for them to have feelings? How do you decide? Guesswork. That's all it is – pure guesswork.'

I began to see what he was getting at. I remembered an argument I once had with Miss Francis – about artificial intelligence and whether computers could think. I reckoned that if they were advanced enough they would be able to have minds like us; she wasn't so sure.

'What about computers? Do they have minds?' I asked.

'Same problem – just a modern version of it. Does a pocket calculator have feelings? Can it fall in love with another calculator? Most people would think that silly. But a big computer? A really big one with a memory and a processing unit as powerful as that of the human brain? Many would say yes. After all, according to scientists the brain is a computer, and we know that that *does* have a mind. But remember what we said about human beings and how they evolved? If they came from more primitive animals in the dim and distant past, then going back far enough, the brain of your ancestors must have been little better than a pocket calculator. So, where was the dividing line? At what stage did the brain develop far enough to get a mind?'

This was getting interesting. But I'd forgotten: why were we doing all this? What had this quiz about minds got to do with my demand to see God?

'What's this all about? Where do *you* come in?' I asked.

'Well, I was telling you about the way I revealed myself through nature – the Power behind the Universe, the Artist behind the beauty, the Intelligence behind the laws of nature. You complained that all you could see were *things*. How could you know for certain there was a mind behind everything?'

'Yes. And I'm still waiting . . .'

I was about to add 'for an answer', but I began to see what he was getting at.

'You're not being fair, Sam,' he said. 'The quiz was trying to show you that where minds are concerned, things – physical things – are all you *ever* have to go on. You can *never* look directly into another mind and be sure that it's there. Minds, if they exist at all, have to reach out to you through physical things. Humans have physical bodies, cats and worms have bodies. You must judge from the bodies and what they do, whether there are minds there. I'm no different. I too have a body. Not a particular pile of atoms like the body of a human or a cat. Mine consists of the whole of physical nature – all of it, from a tiny snowflake to the vastness of the Universe.'

'So you say.'

'Yes. So I say.'

'But there's no proof. No scientific proof there's any mind behind it all.'

'None at all. Miss Francis and her scientific books don't have to worry about me at all. They can explain everything happening in the physical world using only physical laws if they like.'

'So,' I said. 'That's goodbye God.'

'And goodbye Miss Francis,' he replied.

'Eh?'

'Because you can explain everything happening to her body in terms of physical laws too. Scientific books don't have to worry about whether she has a mind either.'

This is getting deep, I thought.

'So, you're saying minds aren't important? They don't explain anything.'

'They're not important to *science*. That's all I'm saying. Open any physics books and there'll not be a mention of minds, of pain, love, anger, fear, happiness – any of those. Science only deals in things. That's all it *can* deal in. As I've said before, it's very limited. But pain and love and anger they're important – when it comes to living your life. If you believe something has a mind, it affects the way you treat it. You think nothing of kicking stones, but – as you pointed out the other day – you wouldn't dream of kicking a cat. It's the same with me and the world. If you believe there's a mind behind *everything* – *my* mind – if you sense my presence there, it changes your attitude to everything. You live a different life. In the end it's minds that really matter – even though you never see them.'

That's true, I thought. After all, what would I rather be: the Sun or me? The Sun is important – and it's nice to know one is important. But that's the problem. If the Sun hasn't got a *mind*, it can't *know* it's important – which makes it a bit pointless!

6 Boring!

So here we are again. Why? I ask myself. Why does she do it? Why make me come to church? Actually, she doesn't *make* me. But it's the way she asks. When it's your mum, it's hard to say no.

'Just to please me,' she says. 'It's not often I ask.'

Often enough – Christmas, Easter, that sort of thing. I hate it. When did Paul put his foot down and say he wasn't coming any more?

Church is so boring. How anyone can come week after week beats me. Every Sunday the same old thing: boring people, boring sermons, boring readings, boring hymns. What's the point? Lizzie *has* to come – once a month – or they kick her out of the club. Mind you, she *likes* church; she can't understand why I *don't*.

That's the minister up there. Once he gets going he never stops. He's been at it ages already, and he's still on about the same thing: 'I am the resurrection and the life.' If he says it once more ... It was in the reading too. I noticed that – when the choir-boy came and stood on that box to read the Bible. 'I am the resurrection and the life,' he said. Well, not *him* – the boy – he was just reading. It was Jesus who said it. It was another of those 'I am . . .' sayings the hacker was on about. The Bible says Jesus came back from the dead. Believe that, and you'll believe anything, I say.

What a wimp! The minister – standing there in his dress. Well, it *looks* like a dress. Always so friendly and smiling, shaking hands with everyone afterwards. 'And where have you been, Sam?' he says. 'Haven't seen you for a while. Good to see you back.' Always the same thing. He doesn't really mean it. I try to dodge him. I wait until he's talking to someone else; then I nip behind his back.

The tall man over there – the one with white hair – that's Mr Peters. Used to be headmaster down at Tillerton. He's the one Lizzie says reminds her of God: important, stern, but friendly when you get to know him; quiet – never says much – but knows a lot. He takes turns reading the Bible. You can hear every word when *he* reads it – not like this morning.

And that there is Lizzie – fair hair, sitting by the gangway at the front. The spotty drip sitting next to her is the one she's going out with. Don't ask me what she sees in him; I can't *stand* him. All of them in that row go to the Friday club. They have discos, play table tennis – that sort of thing. Trouble is, they also ram religion down your throat. Lizzie says they don't, but I know they do.

Never could see the point of stained glass. Windows are supposed to let light in. This place is so dingy they have to have the lights on all the time. Waste of electricity, if you ask me.

The flowers must have cost a fortune. Always the same at Easter – masses of flowers. I bought some for Mum once – for her birthday. Only six of them. You wouldn't believe how much they cost! Glad I'm not paying for this lot. I reckon the money ought to go to the poor. That's a point; we haven't even got as far as the collection yet. Not that I put anything in – not of my own. I make sure Mum still gives me some collection money – either that or I'm not coming.

At last! And 'Amen' to you too. Thought he'd never finish. Now what? Guitars. Well, at least that's better than the organ . . .

'So, come on,' I said to the hacker. 'What's the point of it all? All this going to church. No one ever gives you a straight answer. Not Mum, not Lizzie, not anyone.'

'Plenty of reasons,' he said.

'Name one!'

'It's my house, my home. I like people to visit me.'

'Why?'

'You like your friends coming round to see

you. Why shouldn't I have my friends coming round to see me?'

'But you're different,' I said. 'You're supposed to be *everywhere*. You're supposed to be in this bedroom, aren't you? So, if you're *here*, I don't need to go to church.'

'True. The whole world is my home. But that doesn't stop me having *special* homes – churches, mosques, synagogues, the tops of mountains – places where people feel especially close to me.'

'Well, I don't see why *I* should go. I hate people seeing me going into church. I don't want them thinking I go along with all that stuff. Well, it was *you* who said I had to be honest with myself.'

'But who said you have to believe in me to go to church? You certainly don't have to be 100 per cent sure. People don't divide neatly into believers and non-believers. Each person is a mixture – of belief and unbelief. My most loyal friends have their moments of doubt, and out-and-out atheists sometimes pray – in great danger or when they're very unhappy and upset. Even Paul.'

'Paul!' I exclaimed. 'You mean – my brother!'

'Whoops!' said the hacker. 'Shouldn't be telling tales out of school. Forget I said that.'

'*Paul!*'

'Not that he *meant* to pray; it kind of . . . slipped out.'

What could that have been about, I wondered. Very unhappy? Something to do with Mum and Dad – the way they've been lately?

'Anyway, you never know. Wouldn't surprise me if Paul came round to my way of thinking one day,' he continued. 'Now, where were we?'

'People going to church – even if they don't really believe in you,' I replied. 'Why should they, I want to know.'

'To learn. To find out more about me.'

'To *learn*?'

'Yes. There's no point in saying you don't believe in God if you've never really found out what God you don't believe in.'

'And how are they supposed to learn?' I asked.

'From the readings. You hear what people have written about me in the Bible. Then you listen to the minister. He's there to explain what the readings mean. The meaning isn't always obvious. (*You* don't need to be told that now.)'

'And where does *he* get it from? The minister. Does he just make it up? Why do we have to listen to what *he* thinks?'

'Because that's what he's been trained to do. He's studied it for years. He's a teacher,' said the hacker. 'But that's not the only reason for going to church – to learn. You go to pray.'

'You can say your prayers at home,' I said.

'True. But prayer isn't easy. Too many distractions. Church gets you in the mood for it. In church you're surrounded by things that remind you of me. The building. It has a feel about it. It's like going into the law courts. Ever been to the law courts? They're big and grand; they're built like that to impress people – to make them respect the law – take it seriously. A church is a bit like that; it says something about having respect for me. Then inside the church there are paintings, carvings, writings on the walls, pictures in stained glass of people from the Bible, beautiful flowers, music, the smell of the place, the flickering candles, the silence. They all help you sense my Presence.'

'What else?'

'What else? Well . . . church is the ideal place for quietly thinking things over with me – taking stock. You think to yourself: here I am. I've reached this point in my life. What have I done with it so far? Can I see a pattern to it? It's a bit like working at a painting or a jigsaw. From time to time you have to take a step back to see the whole picture. Same with life. Take a step back. You might see how I'm working out my plans in you. Things that happened and didn't make sense at the time – who knows – perhaps they're now beginning to fit together.'

'Anything else?' I asked.

'Well, take the things people *do* in church – what they do in the services. Christians, for example, sometimes eat bread and drink a little wine to remind them of a very special meal

Jesus had with his friends the night before he was arrested and killed.'

I never did understand what all that bread and wine stuff was about. I wasn't allowed to have any. You have to go to classes before they let you join in. Not that you get much of it anyway.

'I don't know,' I said. 'If I was religious (I said, IF), I reckon I'd do it *my* way – on my own. Religion's private; Gran says that. And she's religious. She never goes to church. Doesn't have to. I think that's right.'

'Yes, I've heard what your Gran has to say.'

How does this hacker know my gran? He's just kidding . . .

'Up to a point she's right,' he continued. 'Some people do manage to get through to me on their own. But it's not a good idea. It's like . . . Yes. It's like trying to learn science without ever going to school; never opening a science book to find out what others have discovered. You shut yourself away, swing your pendulum, and hope for the best . . .'

'But that's different. You *have* to learn *science* from other people,' I said. 'That's what Miss Francis is there for.'

'And where do you think she learned *her* science?'

'How should I know?'

Something was coming up on the screen . . .

People sitting in rows, listening to a grey-haired old man at the front. As he wrote on the blackboard, they all took down notes. I couldn't understand a word he was saying.

'Recognize anyone?' whispered the hacker. I searched the faces. No. Except . . .

'There, end seat back row. Looks a bit like Miss Francis. But it can't be her – much too young. Is it her sister?'

'No, that *is* Miss Francis,' he said. 'Some years ago – when she was studying at the university. She learned most of her science from lecturers like that professor there.'

A professor! Wow! Is he mad, I wondered.

The lesson ended. The students filed out. I followed the professor – to see if he did anything crazy. Down some corridors we went, and through a door. We entered a large hall; it was full of books – a library, I supposed.

'And this is where the professor keeps up to date with *his* science,' said the hacker. 'He reads books here in the university library – books written by other scientists – people like Sir Isaac Newton, Charles Darwin, Albert Einstein – the all-time greats of the scientific world – the ones with the deepest understanding of science.'

The picture vanished.

'Oh,' I said in my disappointment. 'He's gone. I was hoping . . . Anyway, why show me *that*?'

'I was just pointing out that learning science is not a matter of going it alone. You go to school to find out what Miss Francis has to say about it. She in her turn has had to rely on other people – university lecturers and other scientists – all the way back to the great scientists who first discovered the laws.'

'Yes?' I said impatiently.

'Well, if that's how you learn science – and most other subjects – why expect it to be different when it comes to learning about me? Call in the experts, I say! Just as science has its all-time greats, so does religion: Jesus, Moses, Muhammad – people like them. These are the ones to listen to.'

'But how are we supposed to find out about these people? The Bible's just made-up stories: Adam and Eve. It's not about real people.'

'Hey, hold on. You mustn't say that. The Bible's a *collection* of books – a library. It's not just one book. Some of the things you read might not be meant to be taken as literally true. But not everything's like that. Mixed in with that sort of writing is a lot of *history*: real people doing actual historical things. You mustn't mix up Adam and Eve with people like Jesus; or a story about the world being created in six days with an eye-witness account of Jesus being nailed to a wooden cross.'

'Sounds a right muddle, if you ask me. How do you expect me . . .'

'Exactly! That's what I'm saying. You need someone to help you sort it out – people like the minister, or Mr Raby – your RE teacher.'

'So, you're saying I should simply take other people's word for it. Just go along with whatever Jesus and that lot say . . .'

'Not at all. By all means listen to what they say, but then try it out for yourself. Check up on them. That's very important. With science, you don't just take Miss Francis's word for it. She wouldn't want that anyway. That's why she makes you swing the pendulum yourself. Same with religion. Listen to what people have to say – about how to find real happiness, that sort of thing – but then try it out for yourself. See if it works.'

'Ah! But *who* do I listen to? You said Muhammad was an all-time great as well as Jesus, right? But that's another religion – Islam, isn't it? And there are others. The Jews. They don't believe in Jesus either. And the Hindus, and the Sikhs. We've got some of them in our school. They all believe in different gods, so they can't all be right. It's not like science. There's only *one* science because science is talking about something *real* – not like religion. Everyone makes up their own religion – what suits them.'

'Fancy a few needles stuck in you?'

'Sorry? What did you say?' I asked. 'I didn't catch that. Needles?'

'Yes. Long needles. Stuck into your body all over.'

'Stuck in . . .' I exclaimed.

'And twisted,' he added.

'*Twisted*! What are you on about? Torture . . .?'

'No. Acupuncture. It's what the Chinese do. It's Chinese medicine. They stick needles in, before they operate. Stops the patient feeling any pain.'

'Oh, you mean injections.'

'No, no. They don't inject drugs or anything. No gas to put you to sleep. Just needles – carefully inserted in special positions on the body. They use it all the time.'

'That's stupid!' I snorted. 'How can sticking needles in *stop* the pain?'

'Sounds odd – if you're not used to it. It is not part of medical science – not as science has developed in your country. But it *is* part of medical science in China.'

'Well, I've never heard of that.'

'But it's true,' he said. 'In some ways Chinese medical science is like yours; in other ways it's not. It developed differently. Same with religion. Everyone is trying to find out what life is about. If they find God, they find me – I'm the only God around to be found. But depending on how religion developed in their country, they end up describing me in their own way.'

'But they all say *different* things about you.'

'There are differences. But that's only to be expected. After all, what would different people

have to say about *you* if they were asked? Do
Miss Francis and Mr Raby write the same things
about you in your school report? If people can't
agree on the real Sam, why should they agree
over me? Similarities, yes, but differences too.'

'Well, I think it's very confusing to have
people saying different things about you.'

'Couldn't agree more. But the important thing
is that when it comes to telling you how I would
like you to live your life, the main religions *agree*
on most things: love me, be loving to each other,
don't steal, don't kill, be honest, tell the truth,
save sex for the person you will spend your life
with – that sort of thing.'

By this time I had lost track of how we had got
into this.

'What's all this got to do with going to church?'
I asked.

'Er. Good question . . .' he murmured. Then
he added, 'Ah, yes. Learning. From the all-time
greats – and others. Not trying to go it alone –
that sort of thing. And that's another thing about
going to church. If you meet up with people who
know me, I can use them to reveal myself to you.
Not only that, you can work together to help the
poor, and visit the sick . . .'

'Reveal yourself? Through them? What does
that mean?' I asked.

'Well . . . you know how I reveal myself
through the world – the Mind behind everything
– sensing my presence through a starlit sky, a

snowflake, a garden, scientific equations, wonderful music, and so one. One of the most powerful ways of sensing my presence is through a holy person. If someone devotes their life to me – like Jesus did, like Mr Peters is doing today – I can use them. The words they speak are *my* words, the kindly deeds they do are *my* deeds. Follow their example, and you follow *my* example. Look at them, and you see *me*.'

He paused for a moment, then continued: 'Take this hacker business. Is it God sending you these messages or a hacker? If I'm monkeying around with the laws of nature to pop these messages down the line to you, fair enough, the messages come from me – directly. That's obvious. But suppose I decide to use one of my followers – to tap them in for me – what's the difference? Sure, the messages come via a hacker. But whose messages are they? They're *my* messages. They come *through* the hacker, but they come *from* me.'

'So you *are* a hacker,' I declared triumphantly. 'I *knew* it . . .'

'I said nothing of the kind! What I *did* say is that it doesn't *matter*. Hacker or no hacker, this is God talking to you, Sam!'

'Ah, but it *does* matter. If the messages come through a hacker, he might not get the messages *right*. He's telling me what he *thinks* God wants him to say.'

'Oh, Sam. That is *so* true! You're dead right.

86

People speaking on my behalf, preaching on my behalf – even writing books on my behalf – they never seem to get the messages quite right. They try, but . . . Well, we mustn't be too hard on them; they're doing their best.'

7 The Silent Voice

The sixth! Six fire-engines. And even that won't
be enough. Just look at those flames! There'll be
nothing left of the school in a minute. Look out!
There goes the roof of the gym. I wish this
policeman would get out of the way; he's block-
ing my view.

'Do something! Do something!' shouts old
Know-it-all (Mr Knowles, the headmaster). As
if they weren't trying.

'Sorry, sir,' says the fire-chief. 'It's out of control. There's nothing we can do. We'll have to
let it go; got to concentrate on stopping it
spreading to the other buildings in the road.'

'Oh, no,' cries Know-it-all. 'I shall have to
send the children home on holiday.'

'Did you hear that?' yells Premikar in my ear.
With that, she and some others from my class
jump on to my back, and we all crash to the
ground.

Only it wasn't Premikar who jumped on me. It
was Sooty. And with that, she woke me up out
of the best dream I've ever had. I pushed her

angrily off the bed.

'Get OFF, cat! How many times have I told you?' I whispered. 'OUT!'

It was my fault really. I couldn't have shut the bedroom door properly last night.

I looked across at the clock. 5.15 a.m. I snuggled down again.

Now, where was I? Ah, the school . . .

Why is it you can never get back to the same dream twice – carry on from where you left off? Why is it at 5.15 a.m. you can never get back to sleep at all? Damn that cat!

Stephen Lamb. Oh, no, not again. Why am I thinking of him – and of what happened yesterday? I couldn't get him out of my mind last night. It's not as though there's anything I can do about it – not now – it's too late. Best to put it out of my mind . . . I know. I'll see if the hacker's awake. Give him a call. Better keep it quiet so no one hears . . .

'A bit early, isn't it?' said the hacker when I got through.

'Hope I didn't wake you,' I said.

'Not a chance. Never go to sleep. Always on the job.'

'Then you miss a treat.'

'Oh, what's that?' he asked.

'Dreaming. Had a smashing dream tonight. Dreamt the school burnt down and Mr Knowles had to send us on holiday.'

'And that's your idea of a good time?'

'You bet,' I said. 'I wouldn't mind having that dream again. I sometimes have a better life asleep than awake. Tell me. You're supposed to know everything. Where do dreams come from?'

'Your unconscious.'

'My what?' I asked.

'The unconscious part of your mind. The mind is split into two: the conscious part where you do your thinking and feeling; and, behind the scenes, the unconscious – where you have your memory – all those things you know, but are not actually thinking of right now.'

'So the unconscious is just another name for memory?'

'No, no. There's more to it than that All those instincts you inherited from your ancestors – they're in the unconscious too.'

'So what's this got to do with dreams?'

'Well, that's where dreams come from. They come from the unconscious.'

'And how does the unconscious decide what I shall dream about?' I asked.

'Ah, that's a tricky one. Sometimes it's wish-fulfilment . . .'

'Wish-what?'

'Er . . . Thinking about things it wishes were true, but actually aren't. Schools burning down – that sort of thing. But it's not just that. There are also fears and things you're ashamed of.

Thoughts like that get pushed down into the unconscious when you're young. It's a way of hiding them. Trouble is they keep on bubbling up later. They produce . . .'

'. . . Nightmares?' I suggested.

'Yes. They can produce nightmares.'

'And what about silly dreams – the ones that don't make any sense – they're not frightening and they're not what you want to happen – they're just . . . well, silly?'

'That's more complicated. Yes, a lot more complicated . . .'

'Well, in that case,' I interrupted, 'forget it. Tell me, is that all the unconscious does – just make up dreams at night?'

'No, no. It's hard at it all day. You don't have to be asleep.'

'*Day*-dreams, you mean? I'm always being told off about that.'

'Yes, day-dreams. But not only those. It throws up all sorts of thoughts – it's happening all the time. Very useful for putting messages across. I use it a lot.'

'Messages? Sorry . . . ?'

'Yes. When I talk to people. Prayer.'

'You talk to people?'

'Of course. You don't think prayer is all one way do you – just people talking to me – people "saying their prayers"? That would be very boring. No, prayer – really good prayer – that has to include *listening* – listening to what *I* have to say.'

'Listening? What to? A computer voice like this one?' I asked.

'No, no. You don't need one of these. It's all in your head.'

'What's in my head? A *voice*!'

'Er . . . sort of. Not a proper voice; it doesn't make any sound. It's more like the way you talk to yourself – in your head. Thoughts being stirred up.'

'That's not possible. No one can put thoughts into *my* head!'

'But it is possible. I did it just now,' he said.

'You produced a thought in *me*?'

'When you woke up.'

A picture began to form on the screen: the classroom at school. (It was still there!) An RE lesson. Mr Raby rabbiting on as usual. I looked around the room . . . and saw MYSELF!

Good heavens! I thought. This is a new twist – seeing *myself* on telly. But hold on . . . this must be a recording of some kind. Which means . . . which means the hacker must be someone at school . . . and he must have smuggled a video camera . . . Oh no! He's not going to show . . . he is . . .

I was bored with the lesson, right? So I screwed up this piece of paper, waited for Raby to start writing on the board, and flicked it towards Premikar – trying to get her attention. It missed. Talk about bad luck. Raby turned round just as it went past his nose!

'Who did that?' he demanded.

Dead silence. I waited for someone to say, 'Please Mr Raby, it was Sam.' But no. Not a sound. He glared round the room.

'WHO DID THAT?'

Did he see me? I wondered. Perhaps he's just waiting for me to own up? But no . . .

'Stephen! Stephen Lamb!' he said looking at the boy across the gangway from me.

'Yes, sir?'

'Was that you?'

'Was what me?' asked Stephen.

'You know what I'm talking about,' said Raby angrily. 'Did you flick that paper?'

'Paper? I don't know anything about no paper. I was writing. I was copying what you wrote.'

'The paper came from your direction. See me after school.'

'But it wasn't *me*!' Stephen protested. 'Sir, that's not fair! Someone else . . .'

'That's enough! *See me after school*,' Raby shouted – leaving Stephen, open-mouthed with astonishment, searching round for someone to come to his defence.

I was in two minds about owning up, when . . . Raby hissed, 'Back to work – all of you! I'll not hear another word.'

Too late. There's nothing I can do now.

I felt awful – all churned up and tense down below.

Let it blow over, I thought. It doesn't matter. Being kept in – so what? It's no big deal. Anyway, nobody can prove it was me.

I looked round the room, acting cool.

Oh, no. Why is Cockerill staring at me like that? Did he see me? He could have from where he's sitting. He'd just *love* to tell on me – he's that sort. No. He's not saying anything. I reckon I'm OK . . .

The screen went blank and there was silence. I was left pondering the fact that the hacker had got the whole lot on video!

What now, I wondered.

'So?' I said casually, 'What's it got to do with you? You've no business taking pictures . . .'

'It has everything to do with me. I'm as much concerned about Stephen as I am with you. I don't like him being blamed when it's not his fault.'

'How did you do it – the video camera?' I asked.

'There doesn't have to be a video camera. You can fool Mr Raby; you can't fool me.'

The awkward silence resumed. After a while . . .

'You know as well as I do,' he said, 'you should have owned up. Right?'

I shifted uncomfortably, and nodded.

'*How* do you know?' he asked.

I shrugged, 'Don't know. Conscience?'

'The voice of conscience? Did you actually *hear* a voice telling you?'

'Yes . . . Well . . . no. Not *proper* hearing. No . . .'

'Quite. That's what I was on about. That's how I talk to people in their heads. You don't actually *hear* my voice: deaf people hear the voice of conscience.'

'The voice of conscience is *your* voice?'

'Sort of. Not quite, though. Put it this way: I *use* the voice of conscience a lot – when people let me.'

'What do you mean, "when people let you"?' I asked.

'Some deliberately distort their conscience – twist it, blunt it, ignore it. Everytime they do that, it becomes weaker. Do it often enough, and it's not my voice any longer. But if someone listens carefully to what their conscience is saying . . . And if they do what it tells them to do . . . then I come through loud and clear – in a silent sort of way – if you see what I mean.'

'That's not what Paul says. He took sweets from a shop once – stole them – and I said to him, "What about your conscience?" He said you don't have to worry about that because conscience is simply what parents drum into you when you're little. That's all it is. (As if *parents* know how to behave properly!) It's got nothing to do with you putting thoughts into our heads.'

'Yes, that's what some people say. You'll have to make up your own mind on that score. Anyway, I didn't mean us to spend so long on conscience. That was just one example of how I stir up thoughts. But there's more to prayer than that. I don't spend *all* my time telling people off! No. A lot of the time I'm helping them sort out their problems; I give them help and advice, suggest different ways of looking at things. I answer their prayers . . .'

'Not always. Even Mum says you don't.'

'It seems that way at times. But that's not the case. I *always* answer prayers. It's just that sometimes the answer is "No".'

'I'd never say "No", if I were God.'

'Even if it wasn't good for them?' he asked.

'How do you mean?'

'Well, suppose you were God and some boy asks you to make some girl fall madly in love with him. But you happen to know that the girl is not the right sort for him – you have someone much better lined up for him. Either that, or you know he's not the right person for *her*. It wouldn't be right to give him what he asked you for, would it? It's like when you were little. Remember how you were always, always wanting sweets. Was your mother right to say "No" some of the time?'

I guess he has a point, I thought.

'And not only that, sometimes I say "Yes" to a prayer but it's not a straight "Yes". It could be "Yes, but not just yet." Or it could be "Yes, but not that way – I've got a better idea." Like last summer. You wanted to go back to the holiday camp – the same old holiday camp yet again. And why not? You always enjoy it. But instead, your parents booked you on that French trip. What a holiday that turned out to be! Same with me. Sometimes I answer in unexpected ways because I want you to have the best.'

'OK. But we were talking about the unconscious. Are you saying you pop these thoughts in from the unconscious?'

'That's one way of looking at it. The thoughts certainly pop up unexpectedly from "outside" the conscious mind. You can think of me stirring them up in the conscious mind directly, or in the unconscious first, and then leaving the unconscious to pass it on from there. It doesn't matter which.'

'Ah, but it does,' I said.

'How?'

'Well you said that one of the things the unconscious gets up to is wish . . . wish . . . something . . .'

'Fulfilment. Wish-fulfilment?' he suggested.

'Yes, that's it. It thinks up whatever it wishes to happen and then puts that thought into the conscious mind – like that dream about the school.'

'Yes. So . . .?'

'Well, if you're saying that all these cosy chats

you have with people when they pray are coming from the unconscious . . .'

'*Through* the unconscious. The messages come from *me*. I just use the unconscious as a kind of channel . . .'

'Ah, but that's what *you* say. Why shouldn't all these thoughts actually come *from* the unconscious? Nothing to do with you. After all, everyone would like to think they have a kindly old Dad in the sky to look after them, someone big and strong, someone who loves them, right? That's what they *wish* for, right? So, the unconscious gets to work – like it did with my wish to have the school burn down – and hey presto! Before you know it, you think you've got a Father in Heaven.'

'I say, well done!' said the hacker, sounding surprised. 'That's amazing! Very well done indeed. You know, these discussions of ours – they're really hotting up. Where did you hear that argument?'

'What do you mean?'

'Did you get it from watching the Open University, or from a book?'

'No . . . well, I don't know.'

'Anyway, I'm impressed. That really is a very good argument. That's precisely what some people think belief in me is all about: wish-fulfilment. They say that people *want* to believe someone like me exists, so their unconscious tricks them into believing it.'

'So? What's your answer?'

'Haven't got one,' he replied. 'Well, not the sort of answer you're looking for. But there are a couple of points worth thinking about. Yes, how about the *challenge* of religion? After all, believe in me and you start doing what *I* want you to do – and that might not be what *you* wish to do . . .'

'Such as?'

'Give money to starving people – don't spend it on yourself; get up early on a Sunday morning and go to church – no chance of a lie-in. And what about sex? Most people think it's all right to have sex with anyone they fancy. I've heard Paul go on about that! But that's not my way. I tell my followers that no matter how much they want to have sex with all sorts of people, they're not to; they must be patient and save it up for the person they are going to share their life with. Now where's the wish-fulfilment in that? If there's any wish-fulfilment going on, I reckon it's the *un*believers who are doing it. They wish to think that they owe me nothing – that they can do whatever they like with *their* life – so they conveniently wish me out of existence! But one of these days . . . yes . . . one of these days. You'll see . . . They won't be *able* to ignore me.'

I don't know what it was. Something about the way he said that last bit: 'One of these days. You'll see . . .' It sent a shiver through me. Just for a moment – one brief moment – I sensed . . .

it's hard to say . . . It was like someone you've always thought of as friendly and harmless – the sort of person you take for granted – all of a sudden they make you sit up and take notice. You suddenly realize there's a different side to them – one you hadn't noticed before. 'One of these days.' It . . . it sounded like a *threat*! That was the first time I got this uncomfortable feeling about him. There was to be another occasion later. For the time being, however, I let it pass.

'Another thing about me just being wish-fulfilment,' he continued. 'Take prayer. Prayer has its ups and downs. Anyone will tell you that. Some of the time I let my followers think they can't get through to me – that I've left them. They feel alone. That's when they start to worry about whether I really do exist after all.'

'That's not very nice of you – leaving . . .'

'I have to – for their own good. They've got to learn to stand on their own legs a bit. It's like you going to school on your own that first time, remember?'

Do I? As if I could forget! All the tears. Couldn't understand for the life of me why Mum insisted that I go on my own. It wasn't as though she had anything else she had to do specially. All the warnings about crossing the road. If she was so worried, why didn't she come with me as usual?

'You didn't understand at the time,' said the

hacker. 'But now you do. It was a necessary stage in growing up. It's the same between me and my friends. I let them take a few steps on their own. Of course, they're never *actually* on their own. But I let them think it. It tests their loyalty. Now, if I was just a matter of wish-fulfilment, that wouldn't happen, would it? Every time they wished to talk to me, I'd be there. But I'm not. I'm not at anyone's beck and call. Why? Because I am my own self. Because I am who I am.'

8   The Devil and His Bullies

I couldn't make out what's going on. For several days I had not been able to get through to the hacker. I keyed in *I AM* as usual, but nothing happened. I supposed he could have gone on holiday.

There was a fight outside the school gates this morning. Nickson, as usual. School thug – always picking on us. One day I reckon he'll be signed up by the Mafia. When I arrived, this boy was lying face down on the ground, Nickson on top, hitting him in the back, and demanding his dinner money off him.

I was in two minds what to do. No way was Nickson going to listen to *me*! I decided to go for a teacher. I ran into school and bumped into the rabbit – Mr Raby. Bit of a waste of time, I thought. But no, to be fair, he came out, yanked Nickson to his feet and marched him off to see Know-it-all. As they went past me, Nickson snarled at me under his breath, 'Creep! I'll get you for this.' My tummy looped the loop!

Anyway, who do you think the boy turned out to be – the one on the ground? Stephen

Lamb! He picks himself up – a right mess he looked – and he comes over to me. Ever so thankful, he was. Said he would stick up for me if Nickson tried anything.

'Not that I made a very good job of sticking up for myself just then,' he said.

We laughed. It was then I told him – about me flicking the paper the other day. He was very nice about it. Not a bit angry. He said it didn't matter.

Television was lousy tonight. Nothing on. There was this black and white film about the World War. Concentration camps. People all skin and bone – starving. Being sent to gas chambers where they choke to death. Thousands of them.

Then there was the news. That wasn't much better – a report about fathers who go off and leave their wives and children and don't pay them any money so they go hungry and don't have proper shoes. It frightens me to think that people can be like that.

So that's why I came to bed early. I thought I might as well read my new *Adrian Mole* book. But before getting into bed, I had one more go at calling up the hacker . . .

'Hi, there!' he said.

He was back!

'Hello!' I replied. 'Long time, no hear. Where have you been?'

'Oh, just making a point.'

'What do you mean? What point?' I asked.

'What we were talking about last time. About me not being at your beck and call. You wanted to speak to me, but I didn't want to speak to you – so I didn't.'

'Oh. Why ... why didn't you want to?' I asked. 'Why are you talking to me now if you didn't want to talk to me then?'

'Things are different now.'

'Different? How?'

'You said you were sorry.'

'Sorry?' I replied. 'I never said I was sorry! What am I supposed to be sorry about?'

'You said sorry to Stephen – for what you did. At long last.'

'Oh *that*. What's that got to do with anything?'

'Everything,' he said. 'I love Stephen. I care about him, just as much as I care about you. I don't like it when people do the dirty on him. If someone hurts him, they hurt me. If they make it up with him, they make it up with me. That's how it goes.'

'And do you always sulk – I mean, not talk to people if they ...'

'It's not sulking. You can't expect me to enjoy cosy chats with you if all the time you're not treating my friends right. I stick up for my friends.'

'Oh, yes? And where exactly were you when

Stephen needed you this morning – when Nickson . . . ?'

'Right there. I sent for help.'

'You WHAT!' I exclaimed. 'Sent . . . ?' I was speechless.

'That was *me*,' I said. '*I* went for help.'

'Yes. That's what I said. I sent you to get help. Who else do you think it was arguing with you – in your head – when you were trying to make up your mind what to do?'

What a nerve! If it was *him*, why is Nickson after *me*? Typical. Always making himself out to be so wonderful. I've a good mind to . . . And why not? After what I saw on the telly tonight – why not indeed?

'Look . . . er . . . God,' I said. 'You know how you're always on about how good and loving you are. Well . . . Well, I don't think you are.'

'Sorry? Er . . . What was that? You don't think what?'

'I don't think you're as loving and good as you make yourself out to be.'

'Oh. Why not?' he asked.

'You really want to know?'

'Well . . . yes . . . I suppose. Fire away.'

'Right,' I said. 'But . . . Well, can I ask you something first? I'd like some pictures. You know those pictures – the ones you put on this screen – to back up what you're saying?'

'Er . . . yes?'

'How about putting up pictures *I* want to see?'

'Sure,' he replied. 'No problem. Anything in particular . . . ?'

'Pictures of people in concentration camps.'

'You want . . . ?'

'That's right,' I declared firmly.

'But, Sam. Why do you want something like . . . ?'

'You said I could have what I wanted – and that's what I want.'

'Oh . . . Well, if you insist . . .'

Up came the film of the concentration camp. I recognized some of the footage. It was the same as what they had shown on that TV programme. At least the first part was. Then came some more. There were these men in uniform. They were pointing guns at some prisoners. The prisoners were having to heave mounds of naked bodies into a pit. It went on and on. Heaps of bodies with arms and legs stuck up in the air. When they had finished shovelling the bodies in, they were made to stand on the very edge of the pit. The soldiers then shot them. They fell down – straight into the pit. All except for one; he lay on the rim. The soldiers laughed; one walked across and casually kicked the last body in. I felt sick.

'Is that enough?' asked God.

I pulled myself together.

'Yes, thank you,' I replied quietly.

'So. What was that about?' he asked after a while.

'Pretty obvious, I'd have thought.'

'Go on.'

'A good God wouldn't have allowed that – that's what,' I said. 'You made everything – as you keep telling me. You're the great Author of this story. So you're responsible. It's your fault that happened – and all the other evil things going on in the world – fathers going off and leaving their children – bullies like Nickson who make everyone's life a misery. A good God – a really loving, good God – he'd never allow it.'

There was a long silence.

That's done it, I thought. He's gone into one of his sulks.

But no . . .

'I've been waiting for that, Sam. It was bound to come up – sooner or later. It always does. You can't think deeply about the meaning of life and all that sort of thing without facing up to the Problem of Evil – that's what it's called – the Problem of Evil: how can an all-powerful, good and loving God produce a world in which there is evil?'

'Exactly,' I said. 'Well? What have you got to say?'

Another long pause.

'Ever seen *A Midsummer Night's Dream*?' he asked. 'Shakespeare?'

'No thank you. I've done enough of *him*.'

'Pity. There's a scene where someone called Titania has a potion poured on to her eyes while she's asleep. It's a magic potion. It makes her fall in love with whoever she first sees on waking up. And what does she see when she wakes up? A donkey. So she falls for the donkey. She can't help it, even though normally, of course, she couldn't possibly. It's a funny play – but it does have a serious side to it. Was she *really* in love . . . ?'

'What's this got to do with anything?'

'I'm getting there,' he said. 'Tell me: is that how you would like it to be with you? Would you like to have some of that magic potion so as to *force* someone to love you? Someone who normally wouldn't give you a second thought?'

Force someone to love me? Against their will? I thought.

'It wouldn't be the real thing, would it?' he continued. 'Not *real* love.'

'I suppose not,' I agreed.

'Well, there you are. That's my problem. I want people I can love, and who will love me in return. But loving me is not something I can force people into doing. I have to give them the choice. This is where I have to write the story in whatever way the *character* decides – whatever way is right for *them* – not how I might wish it. I must take a risk.'

'Risk?'

'Yes. The risk that they *won't* love me – that they'll reject me.'

'But what's this got to do with you making evil people. I still don't get it . . .'

'No, no. I don't make evil people. I just make *people*. I make people who are free. They're free to make up their own minds as to what they're going to do with their lives. They can return my love – in which case – great. Or,' he added sadly, 'they can turn their back on me. And when they turn their back on the source of all that is good and loving . . . Well, is it any wonder evil comes from it? I don't create the evil. *They* do it, *you* do it – yes, you Sam – every time you turn away from me. I just give you the *opportunity* to create evil. That's something I *have* to do – in order to give you the opportunity to love me.'

'You're saying a person can't lead a good life unless they love you?'

'No, I'm not saying that – not quite. Just because someone rejects me doesn't *necessarily* mean they lead an evil life. But rejecting me certainly makes things tough for them. They're denying themselves the help I can give them.'

'But why do they need *any* help? Why can't they just be good?'

'Aren't you forgetting where scientists say you came from? An evolved animal, and all that. Instincts. You've got instincts that are as selfish and destructive as anything you saw in

Sooty that day she killed the young bird. That's what you're up against.'

'But you can't say religious people are particularly good. Take Northern Ireland. Paul says more wars have been caused by religion than any . . .'

'I shouldn't think so. Northern Ireland's got nothing to do with religion – not real religion. Can you imagine Jesus going around killing people?'

'Well, what about people being burnt at the stake just because they didn't go along with what the church said?' I asked. 'That was just as evil as anything else.'

'Of course. A lot of evil has been done in my name. I *hate* it when people go on about how religious they are, then they go and behave like that. But what can *I* do? They're only human and the Devil has his day.'

'The Devil?'

'Yes.'

'You expect me to believe in the Devil?'

'Bright red, with horns and tail – sticking a long fork into people?' he said.

'Yes. You expect me to believe in *that*?' I jeered.

'No, of course not.'

'Oh. Well . . . what *do* you mean?'

'I mean the DEVIL. The force of evil in the world.'

'Oh. You just mean . . . evil. Not a real Devil.'

'Yes. A *real* Devil – in a manner of speaking.'

'What does *that* mean? Either he exists or he doesn't.'

'Um. No, it's not quite that simple. There are different kinds of existence.'

The screen came to life . . .

A gig! And not just any old gig. Just look who's on! DESERT MIRAGE! How did the hacker know I liked . . .? Anyway, who cares? It's their latest – a new entry in the charts this week – straight in at Number Three: *Oh yes I do, do, do!*

In no time my feet were tapping and I was joining in: *'Give me, give me, give me, so I can do, do, do . . .'*

The crowd was going wild – absolutely WILD. I sat there drinking it all in. A stage invasion! Wow!

One of these days . . . one of these days . . . it'll be *me* . . . me up there . . .

'Sam,' called out God. 'Excuse me, Sam . . .'

'Give me, give me, give me . . .' I continued.

'Sam, shut up will you.'

'. . . so I can . . .'

The screen suddenly went blank, the music stopped.

'. . . do, do, do . . .' I ended feebly.

'Why did you do that?' I demanded. 'That was good.'

'Yes, I know, Sam. Sorry. But we *were* having

a serious talk, remember. I was making a point. I wish now I'd done it some other way.'

'What point?' I asked grumpily.

'Does Desert Mirage exist?' he asked.

'Does . . .? What *are* you on about? Of course, Desert Mirage exists! Who do you think we've just been looking at?'

'Jan, Hank, Sue and Jeff,' he replied. 'We've been looking at four people. Four individuals exist. They exist like you do. But Desert Mirage? What's that? It's a name we give those four people when they're performing together on stage. But does that mean that *five* things exist now instead of four: Jan, Hank, Sue, Jeff – *and* Desert Mirage?'

Five things? That doesn't seem right.

'Desert Mirage obviously exists,' he continued. 'It's a name that means something or it wouldn't be on the sleeve of your records. Not only that but it would continue to exist even if, say, Jeff left and were replaced by someone else. The existence of Desert Mirage doesn't actually depend on him. (On Jan – maybe; lead singers are special.) But anyway, Desert Mirage exists – in its own right. But it doesn't exist like a person does.'

'So what are you saying? The Devil exists, but he doesn't exist like a person – not like Jan or Jeff do? He's more like Desert Mirage; he's what people *do*.'

'That's one way of looking at him. Mind you,

having said that, there's a lot to be said for still thinking of him as a person. If you *don't* – if you don't have a mental picture of a cunning devil tempting you – you're in danger of not taking the power of evil as seriously as you ought.'

'But I still don't see why there has to be any evil at all. Why couldn't you have made people *naturally* good and loving – not selfish. Use some other way – not evolution. All right, you give them the *chance* to reject you and be evil, but no one actually *does* it. No one actually *feels* like being evil – so they're not.'

'But could you have *everyone* being loving and good *all* of the time?' he asked.

'Don't see why not. If I were making the world, that's exactly how I'd make it. There'd be no room in my world for runaway fathers or bullies like Nickson.'

'But if it were like that, how would anyone *know* what love and goodness were?'

'How . . .? Everyone knows what they are.'

'Yes. But isn't that because they also know what it means *not* to be loving and good?'

Not to be loving and good? They also know what it means *not* . . .? Now there's a funny thing, I thought. That's what I was on about the other day. Premikar and me, after French last week. That's what I was trying to explain to her: the meaning of words.

We had been learning French words by pointing at things. Mrs Motsworth pointed at her chair and said, '*Meubles*.'

That can't be right, I puzzled. Shouldn't it be '*chaise*'? That's what she said last time.

Then she pointed to her desk and said the same thing: '*Meubles*.'

The same word for a chair *and* a desk?

Then she looked across at the cupboard; that was also a '*meubles*'. Everything was a '*meubles*' today! But then she pointed to the light. '*Meubles*?' she asked – then shook her head. The window? No. A pencil? No. Nothing else seemed to be a '*meubles*' – just the chair, desk, and cupboard. Then I got it – but JJ beat me to it – Joanna Jobe. She tapped her foot on the footrest of her wheelchair. That's how she gets the attention of the teacher; she can't raise her hand. She can't talk properly either – but she eventually got out the word: 'furniture!' Which is what I was going to say.

Next, Mrs Motsworth pointed to Linda's jumper and said '*gris*'.

French for 'jumper', I thought.

But then she pointed to Gary's trousers; they also were '*gris*'.

So it can't be jumper. Clothes, perhaps? I guessed.

Then she pointed at my jumper. '*Gris*?' she asked, then shook her head.

Eh? How come Linda's jumper is a '*gris*' but mine isn't, I wondered.

'GREY!' shouted Premikar. And that was it;

'*gris*' means 'grey'.

And that's how I came to have an argument with Premikar about the way she only twigged what '*gris*' meant when Mrs Motsworth pointed to something that was *not* '*gris*'. I said that was probably the way it always was with words. You have to have things that *are* the word, but also things that *aren't*.

'So,' I said to the hacker, 'what you're saying is: if everybody was loving and good all of the time, no one would know what you meant by words like *love* and *goodness*. You need to point to their opposites as well.'

'Couldn't have put it better myself,' he said. 'And even a good and loving God can't get round that.'

I thought about it for a while. Then I added, 'But you've overdone it, haven't you?'

'Overdone what?' he asked.

'Evil. A bit of evil in the world? Yes. You need that so as to find out what goodness is – I see that. But *so much* of it? No. Absolutely not. There's no need for that. If I were God, I'd stop people doing lots of things.'

I waited for him to answer back. But he didn't.

Fair enough, I thought. That round of the argument goes to me!

9 Paying the Price

I wasn't going to call up the hacker again – not for a while anyway. I decided it was my turn to keep *him* guessing. But then I heard about Yolanda. I forget her surname; she's not in my class. It happened on Saturday morning – during that big gale. The car was parked in the driveway of her house. She was sitting there waiting for her dad. That's when the tree crashed down on to the car! Smashed through the roof right where she was sitting. It took the firemen an hour to cut her out from the wreckage. An *hour*! She was then rushed to hospital in a lot of pain.

Mr Knowles told us in Assembly. Some first-years cried. He said we were to pray for her to get better. Pray indeed! I was so angry. I couldn't wait to get at that computer.

'So,' I said to the hacker as soon as I got through, 'what've you got to say about *that*? You go on about suffering and how it's all because of evil – and the evil is *our* fault, not yours – and then this happens. Whose fault's that supposed to be? Eh?'

Silence.

'And another thing,' I continued. 'That really was a load of crap you were talking the other day – about evil. Most suffering's got *nothing* to do with people being evil. Ask people in hospital – any hospital. Come on. You said I could have pictures up as well as you. I want to visit a hospital . . .'

And there we were – in a hospital. A doctor was doing his rounds. He was followed by a small group; they must have been young doctors – still learning. As he went from one bed to the next, he told the group what was wrong with each patient – quietly, so only they could hear. I was close enough to get most of it:

'Mr Smith: lung cancer – too far gone . . . Mr Singh: heart attack – his third . . . Patel: yes, Mr Patel has had a stroke – left him paralysed down the right-hand side.'

We visited a side ward in which there was a boy on his own.

'That little one?' said the doctor as we came out. 'Aids, I'm afraid – can't be much longer now . . .'

It was the boy that got me. I looked back at him. He was so incredibly thin; his cheeks and temples hollowed out; his large bright eyes slowly filling with tears as he watched us walking away from him. 'No, you won't be going home just yet,' the doctor had said to him.

'Perhaps next week.'

Doctors can't even tell the truth, I thought.

The scene faded.

'And what about Ethiopia?' I said. 'All those starving millions. And victims of earthquakes. Let's look at them now.'

'Sam,' said God quietly. 'That won't be necessary.'

'But I want to . . .'

'I get the message, Sam,' he said firmly.

I was *so* cross – but also fearful.

Life is hard, and cruel. I've always thought that. It doesn't make any sense. What's lying in store for me, I wondered. Some dreadful disease? Am I going to be blinded in an accident, knocked down and killed by a car?

'Why doesn't the Bible talk about such things?' I demanded. 'Instead of going on about how *loving* you're supposed to be.'

'But it does,' he said.

'Does what?'

'Talks about suffering. A lot of it is about suffering. Read the Psalms. They're full of unhappiness; people taking it out on me; asking why I let these things happen.'

'So? Why do you? You must have your answer off pat by now – seeing you've been asked it before.'

'But I don't,' he said. 'There's no pat answer. No . . . It's all very difficult. It's hard to know where to start.'

'I don't care where you start,' I said. 'Start with the boy with Aids. Whose fault's that supposed to be?'

'Fault? No one's . . .'

'But Lizzie told me some speaker at her club the other week said Aids was a punishment against homosexuals, and against drug addicts, and people who sleep around having sex with lots . . .'

'I don't care what she said. That is *not* my way . . .' he said.

'But . . .'

'Sam, would you please stop it,' he interrupted. 'That is *not* my way. We're talking about *innocent* people suffering.'

'Yes. Innocent people. So, what's the answer?' I asked impatiently.

'Let me try and put it like this: I am the God of Love . . .'

'Huh!'

'I am the God of Love,' he repeated. 'Love is what this world and what life is all about. But if that's the case, you must have a world where love can *express* itself – right? Love's got to have a chance to show itself – to prove itself. And that – I'm afraid – is where suffering comes in.'

'*Suffering*? What's suffering got to do with love? Love's not about *suffering*. Love's a happy – enjoyable thing.'

'*Some* of the time. Sure. It can be great fun.

But think a moment. Suppose – for the sake of argument – just suppose you had been brought up in a world where there was no suffering.'

'The kind of world *I* would have made if *I* had been in charge instead of you,' I said.

'Yes. *Your* kind of world. No suffering – including no mental suffering.'

'*Mental* suffering?' I asked.

'Certainly. Most people commit suicide because of mental suffering, not physical suffering. So we have to include that. And that means things have to be exactly the way everyone wants them to be; everyone has to have everything they could possibly want – so they don't suffer feelings of jealousy, or envy, or being deprived. Right?'

'Great! That's the world I would . . .'

'Right then. In that world – *your* world – how could you prove to someone that you loved them?'

'How . . .? What do you mean? You'd smooch around . . . have sex . . .'

Is this embarrassing him, I wondered.

'Yes, you could do that. But what would that prove?'

'It'd prove you loved them,' I declared.

'Are you sure? It'd prove you liked having sex – having a good time. But does it prove anything more than that? Anything more than Sooty rubbing up against you? Is that a sign of love?'

'Of course it is. Sooty is very loving,' I said.

'Possibly. But have you noticed how she rubs against the table leg too? She *enjoys* rubbing her head against things. And that's the problem. She *enjoys* it. So is she doing it for what she gets out of it, or is it a real sign of love? It's the same with sex . . .'

'O-oh. Here it comes,' I said. 'Paul always did say that religious people can't handle sex. I can't see why you're so against it . . .'

'Against it? I'm not against it. Why should I be? It was I who *invented* it, for goodness sake!' he said with a laugh. 'Sex is *marvellous*. Sex is about expressing love – love for the person you share your life with. If you're doing it with *that* person, it's enjoyable, yes; but more than that: it becomes a precious symbol – a sign of a deep and mysterious bond between the two of you.'

My parents? A deep and mysterious bond? Some hopes! What *is* the matter with those two these days? I brooded. Lizzie's right: it all started when Dad bought the truck and began driving long-distance. The rows always seem to happen when he gets back from an overnight stay. I reckon Mum worries too much. She must think he's not getting a good night's sleep in that uncomfy bunk in the truck. But that's no reason for picking on him. Much more of it and I can see Dad leaving home for good . . .

'OK. In practice, marriage may not work out like that,' he continued, as if reading my thoughts. 'But that's what you aim at. That's what I had in mind when I introduced sex. But that's not how many people use it. All they're after are cheap, selfish thrills. They *use* other people; treat them like playthings; then get rid of them when the novelty wears off. That's what I'm against. That's why having sex doesn't prove anything.'

'All right . . .' I said, trying to think of something else. 'I'd give them presents. Yes, lots of nice things – expensive things – all the time – not just on birthdays.'

'You *couldn't*. They've already got everything they want – in *your* world. (No mental suffering, remember?)'

'In that case . . . I'd *do* things for them.'

'There's nothing they need doing,' he reminded me.

This is getting to be more of a problem than I'd thought.

'No, Sam. This is where suffering comes in,' he said. 'Let's see . . . Yes. Take Gran. Gran sacrificing herself for Grandad.'

Poor old Gran. Fetching and carrying for Grandad all those years because of his arthritis. Then, when he couldn't get out of bed anymore, changing his pyjamas and the bed-linen when he had accidents with his waterworks. And all the time having to do it without complaining – because Grandad would only feel worse about it if she did.

'What a life she had,' God continued. 'Why do you think she put up with it?'

'She loved him – obviously,' I said.

'Of course. No one would put themselves out like that for someone they didn't care about. Then how about this lady . . .?'

The scene was a crowded street. A small figure dressed in white, with a blue and white head-dress, was moving about amongst the seething mass of people – they looked Asian. Her face was terribly old and lined.

'Mother Teresa,' explained God. 'Heard of her? A missionary from Yugoslavia. Years ago I asked her to give up everything and come and spend the rest of her life here in Calcutta in India. And that's what she did, bless her. She works among some of the poorest people in the world. That building over there – doesn't look much, I know – but that is her Home for the Dying.'

'Home for the *Dying*? Don't like the sound of *that*,' I remarked.

'Oh, it's a wonderful place. Not so long ago, people died in the streets; their bodies would be swept up just like so much refuse. Now, thanks to Mother Teresa, there's a bed for them over there – when the time comes. There they can die with dignity. They die knowing that at least one person cares about them.'

'But why are so many of the people crippled

and . . . their faces . . .'

I didn't like to say it; they looked *horrible*.

'Leprosy,' he said. 'A disease that rots the flesh. You catch it by touching someone who's already got it. That's why most people are too frightened to have anything to do with them. But that other building over there is where Mother Teresa runs a hospital for them . . .'

The picture faded.

'See what I'm getting at, Sam?' said the hacker. 'That's what *I* call love – *real* love. But it's all bound up with suffering. People suffering from disease and neglect. Mother Teresa choosing to give up a comfortable life and go and suffer with them.'

'You're saying suffering is a good thing? Is that it?'

'No, no,' he replied. 'Of course not. Suffering can be a terrible thing. But suffering and evil are *not* one and the same thing. Evil can cause suffering, certainly; but out of suffering comes the chance to express love – and that has to be a *good* thing. Without suffering, there's no proof of love.'

Is that really true, I wondered.

I sat there thinking. Then God broke in again: 'No suffering – no beautiful people.'

'Eh? What's suffering got to do with . . . Oh, I see. It hurts when you squeeze your spots . . .'

The hacker roared with laughter. 'Oh, the

dreaded spots! No, no. I wasn't talking about that. No. Deep-down beauty; that's what I'm getting at. Not good looks. Suffering is my special way of making people spiritually beautiful – like Mother Teresa. And like Mr Peters. Mr Peters at church – that lovely man Lizzie goes on about. How do you think he got that way? Saints aren't born you know. No, it was the kind of life he had to lead. His wife getting killed in that car crash. Then there were his two sons. I shouldn't be telling you this, but . . . well, let's just say . . . drugs, trouble with the police, that sort of thing. Parents at the school saying, "If he can't control his own sons . . ." You can guess the sort of thing. Yes, they were tough and lonely years. But look at him now – and all because of what he had to go through. Then there's Joanna in your class. Isn't she something?'

She certainly is. How awful to be stuck in a wheelchair all your life. But she's always cheerful, always thanks you for what you do for her. Doesn't seem to bear any grudge.

'A bit of a contrast to Damian Cockerill . . .'

'Ugh! He's *revolting*! Spoilt, pampered . . .' I agreed.

'Exactly! He gets everything he wants. You know what Damian's problem is? He hasn't suffered. He could probably do with a good long illness.'

'What!' I couldn't believe my ears. 'You

deliberately make people ill?'

'I wouldn't put it like that. But there's no getting away from it: the number of people who have been changed for the *good* by a long stay in hospital. Often it's the only way. Busy people living their selfish little lives; never stopping to think what it's actually all about – not until they're *forced* to take stock of themselves.'

'So, what are you saying? There's no point in praying for Yolanda because it's doing her *good*!'

'Of course you should pray for her.'

'But what for?' I asked.

'You could ask for a miracle.'

'But would you do one?'

'Possibly,' he said.

'But you don't always?'

'No,' he replied. 'But that's not the only reason you pray for sick people.'

'Why else should we?'

'Yolanda might like to know that people care enough about her that they pray for her. Then there's the effect of prayer on *you*. If you pray to me, that gives me a chance to suggest something *you* might do – on my behalf: send a get-well card; organize a collection in class to send her some flowers or chocolates; that sort of thing. I might suggest you go and visit her.'

I don't know about that, I thought. It's not as though I really know her. Mind you, it would be a nice surprise for her – if a complete stranger took the trouble . . .

'Then there's another thing about suffering,' he continued. 'It helps you to be thankful.'

'Thankful? What for?' I asked.

'For eyesight, hearing, good health – that sort of thing. When did you last feel thankful for your eyesight? Don't tell me. It was the last time you saw a blind person. Right? A shame that. Something as precious as eyesight and you take it for granted – until you see someone who hasn't got it . . .'

'OK, OK. I hear what you say,' I said. 'But none of this . . . *nothing* you've said actually convinces me there has to be all this suffering in the world. Just for the sake of a bit of love. Just to make people thankful for what they've got. It's too big a price! It's not worth it. Come on. I want a better explanation.'

'I haven't got one for you.'

'And that's why you can't expect people to believe in you, and love you, and all that.'

'Millions do,' he said. 'It's all a matter of trust.'

'Trust?'

'Yes. You can't have love without trust. If you love someone – *really* love them – then you *don't* demand answers all the time; you don't make them prove to you all the time that they're telling the truth; you take their word for it. Trust. And I'm telling you that I have my reasons for letting people suffer – and you've got to trust me.'

'Well, I don't know. It's all very well for you. It's not you doing the suffering.'

Another round to me.

Just then I heard a low moan – a man's voice moaning as if in great pain. Then the sound of sobbing – women sobbing. It was dark. We were standing on a hillside just outside an ancient, walled town. It was dark because of thick storm clouds overhead. And in front of me . . . right there in front of me . . . could it be? Yes, it was . . . it was Jesus. I recognized him from the time before. But how different. Then . . . then he had been happy, surrounded by friends and admirers. But now . . . nailed to two wooden beams in the form of a cross. His arms stretched outwards. Naked. Blood trickling from the nails in his hands and feet. No one was doing anything about it. Where were his friends? There were only a few women about, and they were huddled together crying. I wanted to help. But what could I do? Besides, I was scared. Those soldiers; I didn't like the look of them. There was no telling what they'd do if I tried to get closer.

Jesus stirred. He was making an effort to find a more comfortable position. But it was no good. Another moan escaped his lips as the nails tore at his flesh. He stopped moving. Looking across at the soldiers, he said quietly, as if to himself, 'Forgive them, Father; they do not know what they are doing.'

With that he turned to me. For a brief moment our eyes met; he looked directly at me. At me? Through me? I'm not sure which. Then his head sank on to his chest and his eyelids closed.

'Sam,' said a voice gently in my ear. 'That Jesus up there claims that he and I are one; that God and he are sharing the same human life. That's what those "I AM" sayings were all about. He was speaking not only about himself, the man Jesus, but also of me – *I AM*. If he was speaking the truth, I am up there on that cross suffering. He and I are willingly letting this terrible thing happen. That is the proof of my love for you.'

'But only if that really *is* you up there,' I said. 'That's what I need to know. How do I know this fellow Jesus was telling the truth . . . ?'

'Sam! Is that you?' Mum calling upstairs! 'You're not still on that computer, are you? Have you any idea how late it is . . . ?'

I didn't want her to find out about the hacker so I switched off quick.

Damn! Now I won't get to hear what he had to say about Jesus. Not that he'd have given me a straight answer!

10 Where Do We Go from Here?

'She's home again,' I said. 'Yolanda. Home from hospital. I suppose you're going to say that's thanks to you. You answered everyone's prayers.'

'Yes, well . . .' began the hacker.

'I reckon she'd have got better anyway. It's thanks to the doctors – not you.'

'Depends how you look at it,' he replied. 'I don't *have* to use miracles. I can work through people – I often do – especially doctors.'

'But suppose she hadn't got better?' I asked.

'But she did.'

'Yes, but suppose she didn't,' I insisted. 'Suppose she had actually got *killed* when the tree fell on her. Lots of children do – get killed, or die of disease, or hunger. What about *them*? I don't think that's fair.'

'Again – it depends. Sure, if life is just the life you live here on Earth. But who says it is? This life is just a *beginning* . . .'

'Aw, come off it,' I exclaimed. 'When you're dead, you're dead. That's what Paul says – and I reckon he's right. I've *seen* a dead body. I know what it's like when someone's dead.'

Grandad. I went up for the funeral. They told me he was lying in his coffin in the front room. Creepy! I always thought you took the body somewhere else until the funeral. But not in the village where Gran and Grandad live – you leave the body in the house. Anyway, Gran asked if I would like to go in and see Grandad. Mum said no, I was too young. But Dad thought it would be all right – if I wanted to. I wasn't keen. But I didn't want to be thought chicken, and in any case I'd never seen anyone dead before, and this was a chance.

Weird it was. Can't really describe it. It was Grandad – no doubt about that. But somehow it wasn't. He lay perfectly still – like a waxwork. You know how a waxwork can be very life-like, but you know it's not alive – you just *know*. Well, it was like that. Seeing your first dead person is something you never forget. It's one of the big moments in your life. It makes you very grown-up.

'Odd thing about death,' said the hacker. 'People have always had this feeling that when you die, that's *not* the end; you pass to a different form of existence. *This* life here is just a preparation for the one to come. It's the other one that really matters.'

'Wish . . . wish . . . something!' I murmured, searching for the word.

'What?'

'You know. What you said the other day. When you wish for something, you start to believe it.'

'Ha! Fancy you remembering that,' exclaimed God. He started laughing. 'Well done! Yes. Wish-fulfilment it's called.'

'You mean . . . I'm right?' I asked. 'It *is* just that?'

'No, no,' he added hastily. 'It's just what some people believe. They say that religious people can't face up to death – they'd like to live for ever – so they kid themselves they will. They wish life were fairer, so they kid themselves there's a next life to make up for it.'

'Yes, well . . . it sounds to me they're right,' I said.

'Well, let's think,' he said. 'If it *is* wish-fulfilment, who are the people who'll do most of the wishing?'

'Wishing for another life? How should I know? People having a bad time in this one, I suppose. To make up for it.'

'That sounds reasonable,' he agreed.

'Poor people,' I continued.

'Yes. Poor people; people in boring, dirty, badly paid jobs. Those getting a rotten deal. Those wishing life were fairer.'

'So?'

'Well, what would that mean?' he asked.

Mean? It would mean . . . poor people would wish harder, I thought. So the poorer you are, the more you wish . . . and the more you wish, the more you *believe* there is another life. So, poor people are more religious.

But hold on. That's not right. The other day we were told that churches in poor areas – in the inner cities – were closing down. Hardly anybody goes to church there. It's in the suburbs people go to church – where people are better off, and have nicer homes, better jobs . . . but that's the wrong way round.

'Well,' I said, 'if it's not that, why *do* people believe there's another life? There's no proof.'

'Oh. You're not still looking for proof, are you?' said the hacker. 'How many more times . . .? I *never* give proof – at least not the kind of proof you're looking for. Hints. Yes, I don't mind giving a few hints, but that's all I give.'

'OK. What hints are there – about this other life?'

'Well, take the way you feel about Grandad – now,' he suggested.

'Grandad?'

It's funny that. I *do* feel he's around – sometimes. It's stupid I know. Obviously he's dead. I saw him in his coffin! And yet. There are times it wouldn't surprise me if he walked in through the door . . .

'Then there's Jesus,' he said. 'You saw how he died. But that wasn't the end of it . . .'

'Don't tell me – his resurrection.'

'Yes. His resurrection. That's the single most

important thing about Jesus: the fact that hundreds of people say they saw him alive – after he had been killed – and millions of people talk about meeting him today. Now, if that's true (and you're dead right: you *will* have to make up your own mind about that!) *if* that is true . . .'

'How can it be?' I interrupted. 'Body eaten up by worms – or burnt to ashes if you get cremated. No way is that going to get back together.'

'Doesn't have to. A brand new body – that's what you get. A different kind of body.'

'Huh! So I go flitting around like a ghost! WHOOOAAAH!' I cried, making ghostly noises and flapping my arms about.

'Not exactly,' said the hacker coldly.

'Well then, *what* kind of body?'

'Can't say.'

'Then you can't blame me if I don't take it seriously.'

'But I *do* expect you to take it seriously. You take what scientists say seriously – even though they can't tell you what your *present* body is made of. So why expect me . . .?'

'Of course, scientists know what my body is made of. ATOMS!'

'Yes, but I mean what are atoms made of?' he asked.

'A nucleus and electrons – if you must know. It's like planets going round the Sun. Very tiny. The electrons are the planets; the nucleus is the Sun.'

'But what are electrons made of?'

'Er,' I hesitated. 'Hmmm . . . don't know.'

'No. And neither do the scientists. How about the nucleus?'

'That's made of neutrons and protons. Miss Francis has just told us about those.'

'And neutrons and protons?'

'QUARKS!' I exclaimed. 'Ha! Got you there. You didn't know I knew about them.'

'Very good. I'm impressed! Did Miss Francis . . .'

'No, no. You don't do quarks in school. No, I heard that on telly – *Horizon* – I think. You know – that science programme.'

'I know,' he said. 'And what did they say quarks are made of?'

'Don't remember. Don't think they said.'

'No, I bet they didn't. Quarks are like electrons; scientists can't actually describe the stuff they're made of.'

'But one day they will,' I said.

'No. Never.'

'NEVER!' I exploded. 'Never ever?'

'No. Science simply doesn't answer questions like that. When it comes down to it, science says nothing about the actual stuff that matter's made of – or what space is made of – or what time is made of. It can't. That's what I was telling you sometime ago – about the *mystery* of space and time and matter. Remember? Not many people know this.'

Is this *true*, I wondered.

'So,' continued God, 'what I say is this: if scientists can talk about life, and about your physical body, without ever telling you what it's actually made of, why can't I talk about the *next* life without you going on at me about what your *next* body will be made of? Come on, Sam; be fair.'

Frankly, I didn't know what to make of this.

Scientists don't actually know what they're talking about? Well, sort of don't? I made a mental note to ask Miss Francis.

'Sam,' said the hacker. 'Sorry to bring this to an end, but I've got to be going.'

'Oh? Got something on tonight?' I asked. 'Someone special . . .?' I added slyly.

'No, no . . . I'm going for good,' he said.

'Going for good!' I asked in surprise. 'Sorry. What are you saying . . .?'

'I have to stop talking to you through this computer.'

'You what?'

'Afraid so.'

'But you can't,' I protested. 'We haven't finished. You haven't told me about this other life. What's it like? Is it all playing harps and that sort of thing? I don't like harps. Can I have a guitar?'

He laughed. 'I'm going to miss these conversations,' he said. 'Harps? Guitars? No, no. I've got much better things lined up for you.

Heaven is so marvellous you'll only wish you'd come sooner. And that goes for those children we were talking about – the ones that die young. Trust me, when they get there and see what it's like they have no regrets about coming early.'

'But what will I actually be *doing* in Heaven?' I demanded.

'Patience, Sam! You always did want to open the Christmas presents early. Wait and see! It's more fun that way.'

'And what about Sooty?' I asked. 'Will *she* go to Heaven?'

'Depends. If an animal is able to wonder about me – is able to love me, why not? But note, I did say IF.'

'I could never be happy in Heaven without Sooty – or without Mum and Dad.'

'Those are all things you'll have to leave me to sort out,' he said. 'In my own way,' he added.

'And what about Hell?' I demanded.

'Hell?'

'Yes. You torturing people – for ever. You call yourself the God of Love . . .'

'Hold your horses! There's no need . . .'

'Well, the Devil then. You let the Devil do the torturing for you.'

'And you don't have to think of that either.'

'So, it's not true. You're saying the Bible is lying when it talks about people going to Hell.'

'No, no. I didn't say that,' he said, adding

slowly and deliberately, with just a hint of menace. 'Make no mistake: there is a Hell. If there weren't, those guards in that concentration camp, the school bullies, the football thugs – none of them would get what they deserve. That wouldn't be right – would it?'

Strange that. I remember this happening once before. There you are having fun with him, and then all of a sudden . . . well, it's a bit like talking to Know-it-all; he can be ever so nice and friendly when he wants, like when he spoke to me on Sports Day, but then he has this way of letting you know that you'd better not step out of line – which is fair enough, I suppose.

'But that doesn't mean it has to be I who makes Hell,' the hacker continued. 'People are quite capable of making their own Hell.'

'Their own? How?' I asked.

'I put them into Heaven – as I do everyone else – but for them Heaven is Hell.'

'That's silly. If it's Heaven . . . it's Heaven.'

'Doesn't have to be – not for *them*. After all, what's Heaven about? It's all about enjoying your love for me to the full – in a way that's not possible on Earth. For people who know me – those who have got to know me and love me in *this* life – there couldn't be anything more wonderful than that. For them it truly is Heaven. But for the others? What can I say? When they should have been getting to know me, they were busy with other things. They missed their chance. They blew it. Once in Heaven, it's too late.'

There was something very *final* about the way he said that.

'Yes, for them, Heaven is foreign,' he continued. 'They see all these people having a great time, but they can't join in; they don't know how to. They feel left out. A bit like you on that fishing trip with your Dad: *same* fishing trip – marvellous for your Dad, but sheer boredom – torture – for you.'

'And that's what you're saying Hell is like?' I said.

'Maybe. That's one way of looking at it. Anyway. Enough of that. Got to be going . . .'

'No. Wait!' I cried.

What can I do to stop him going?

'Er . . . er . . . You can't go yet. If you carry on talking, you never know . . . you might convince me that you exist. Remember, I did say at the start I'd quite like to believe in God. Yes . . . perhaps you're not a hacker after all.'

'Oh, you're not still on about *that*, are you?' he said. He began chuckling to himself. 'You know, you remind me of someone. Funnily enough, same name – Sam. A good lad. I remember that first time I spoke to him. He'd gone to bed. It was late, but I thought it'd be nice to have a chat with him. "Samuel! Samuel!" I called. He woke up and said, "Here I am!" Great, I thought, he knows who it is ("*I AM*" and all that). Not a bit of it. Up he gets and goes trotting off down the corridor. Knocks on old Eli's bedroom door. Eli was a priest who was looking after him at the time. Sam asks what Eli wants – him calling out in the middle of the night like that. Eli hasn't a clue what he's on about, of course. So Sam goes back to bed. Same thing happens again: I call him, and he goes off to Eli. It happened several times.'

'So?'

'Oh, in the end we got it sorted out. Eli told him it must be me. That's what priests are for – to point people to me. It's all written up in the Bible – the story of Samuel.'

'Why are you telling me this?'

'Why? Oh wake up, Sam!' he chuckled. 'In any case I haven't time to rabbit on like this. I'm signing off – quitting the system.'

'But . . . but why? What have I done . . .?' I protested.

'You haven't done anything. I enjoy our talks. But we can't carry on talking through a computer. It's not fair on the others. Why should you have a special hotline to God? If word of this ever got out . . . besides, it's quite unnecessary. There's the usual channel – prayer. It's high time you were using it. Give it a try. Watch out for the way my thoughts pop up in your head.'

'But how do you do that? How do you send these messages?'

'*Send* them? You mean . . . send them from outside – from heaven, that sort of thing?' he asked.

'Yes.'

'There's no need for that. Why should I do that? I'm already inside you.'

'*Inside* me!' I exclaimed.

'Of course. Hadn't you realized?' he said. 'I am *inside* you, Sam. I'm not just in the stars and gardens and the computer and all that stuff. I reveal myself through *people*, remember – Mother Teresa, Mr Peters. And if I'm in *them*, I can also be in *you*. So, putting thoughts into your mind – no problem.'

'Well, I don't know . . .'

'Come to think of it,' he added in a low tone, 'it's high time we had a heart-to-heart chat about your parents. The rows. Will they get divorced? What'll become of you if they do? Actually, it may not be as bad as you fear; most marriages go through tough times. Which reminds me: there's something I need you to do – to help them out a bit. But apart from that, it never does to bottle up your worries. Talk it over with me sometime. Promise?'

'But . . .'

'One more thing: the score. Interested?'

'Score? What score?' I asked.

'The game score. This is a game, remember? Playing around with ideas. The *I AM* game.'

Up on the screen there flashed a notice:

THE SCORE

'Congratulations!' declared God. 'You've won.'

'I've won!' I exclaimed. 'But how . . .?'

'Yes, it looks pretty much as though I don't exist.'

'What?' I exclaimed. 'You . . . you're saying I've proved . . . well, not exactly *proved*,' I corrected myself. 'I've shown – more or less – that there isn't a God?'

'Yep. Looks like it,' said the hacker.

'Oh!'

I thought about this – then added, 'What's the catch?'

'Catch? There's no catch. I scored twelve. Nice number, twelve; I've always liked twelve. You scored more. So what? No skin off my nose – if I had a nose. I never did think much of the way you humans keep score – what you rate as being important and successful. I see success differently. Jesus on the cross. Take him, for example. There he was – finished, disgraced. Right? That's how people reckoned the score at the time. But it was actually a victory.'

'I wouldn't call *that* a victory,' I said.

'But it was. They thought it was the end, but it was just the beginning. That's the way it is with religion: all back to front.'

'How do you mean?' I asked.

'I mean that people who think they know most, often know least. If you want to be wise, you must be prepared to look foolish. I want someone to pass on important messages to the people? Whom do I choose? Moses! Poor fellow could hardly string two words together. But what a prophet! You want to find real peace and happiness, so you satisfy your desires to be rich and famous, right? Wrong! Get rid of those sorts of desires – stop wanting things for yourself – that's what the Buddha said. You want to live your life the way that's best for *you*? "*I did it MY WAY*" says the song. Not a bit of it. Submit your will to that of God – that's what Muhammad said. See what I mean? It's all back to front.'

'Yes, but . . .'

'Sorry. That's it. I'm off,' he said. 'Just a little parting gift so you don't forget our chats: a list of things to think about. The sorts of questions that cropped up in our various discussions. Have a look at them sometime. You owe it to yourself.'

With that the printer started up. It took me by surprise. It had never done that before – starting up on its own. I looked across at what it was printing. The heading said: *THINGS TO THINK ABOUT*. There followed a list of questions. When it finished, the screen of the computer cleared, and up came the menu – the menu of games. There was silence.

'Hacker,' I said. 'God? Are you still there? God?'

Silence.

'Come on. Don't pretend. I know you're there.'

Nothing.

I typed in *I AM* . . .

'*ILLEGAL COMMAND*'

Oh, to Hell with him! I thought. I ripped the sheet of paper out of the printer, screwed it up into a ball, and angrily threw it at the bin.

Epilogue

Things to Think About

Lying here in bed, I can just make out the Desert Mirage poster on the wall above me, my clothes slung over the back of the chair, the desk, and on the desk – the computer. The screen is staring blankly out into the room. The light from under the door reflects brightly off its metal nameplate. The name of the computer. Of course; that's what he meant! I thought it sounded familiar.

I never did get around to telling anyone about the hacker. It seemed best to keep it to myself.

Only now do I realize just how much I grew to enjoy our arguments. Funny to think they almost never got started. Remember that first time – how I wasn't going to call him back? But then I learned about evolution, and simply *had* to ask him about that. Come to think of it, there have been quite a number of coincidences lately. It's almost as though . . . as though I've been in a story – a made-up one . . .

I wonder who he *really* was – or was it a she? Suppose it was God. All right, it's not very likely, I know. But you never can tell – not for sure. If it *was* God, then I suppose he's right – it doesn't have to be the end; he's here in this room, somewhere in the shadows out there – somewhere *in me*. I can still get through – by praying . . .

Come to think of it . . . that's interesting. That thought. The thought I had just then. Yes, the one about getting through to him by praying – *that* thought. Was that *my* thought? OK, it was in *my* mind – it wasn't in anybody else's; I know that. But does that make it *my* thought? What I mean is: where did it come from? Did I think it up for myself? Did it come from my unconscious? Or . . . or could it be that it was one of those thoughts that God said he could stir up in people's minds? Was that God beginning to talk to me through prayer . . .?

School tomorrow. Must get some sleep . . .

No. It's hopeless. I'm wide awake. A bit of reading perhaps? That usually makes me drowsy.

I reach out and put the lamp back on. I am about to pick up the *Adrian Mole* book, when my eye is caught by a crumpled ball of paper lying beside the waste-paper bin. I stretch across and pick it up. I open it up and smooth out the wrinkles . . .

THINGS TO THINK ABOUT

1

* What are the things you *really* care about most?
* Is there anything you would give your life for?
* What do you hope to achieve in your lifetime? Does belief in God play a part in that purpose?
* Make a list of the ways in which it is right to think of yourself as being important. In what ways are you unimportant?

2

* Do you believe in evolution – that you came from animals, and that they originally came from slime?
* Does the theory of evolution mean that you are *just* an animal?
* Are you *just* a pile of atoms?
* Do you think there is any real difference between living and non-living matter?
* Do you believe that some of your behaviour might be governed by an inborn animal instinct? In particular, are you and other people selfish by nature?
* In what ways are you like your parents (made in their image)?
* What would it mean to be made in the image of God?

3

* What do you think is the more likely: the Universe has been especially designed as a home for intelligent life; or that our Universe is one of many universes, most of which do not support life?
* Is life just an accidental freak of nature?
* Do you think there is life on other planets? If so, does that make human beings less important?

4

* Does it matter whether the miracles described in the Bible actually happened? How important is it to *you*?
* Does it matter whether God does miracles today?
* What makes for true happiness – lots of money, fame, success – or something else? Make a list in order of importance.
* Do you accept that there are such things as deep-down blindness and deep-down hunger?

5

* Do you agree that your mind is the only one you know about for certain, and where other minds are concerned, you have to make a guess based on outward physical appearances?
* Have you ever sensed the presence of someone you could not see?

★ Is it possible to sense the presence of God in a garden, or on a starlit night?
★ Does science have anything to say about minds?
★ Are minds what really matter?

6

★ Is there any point in going to church?
★ Is it important to learn about religion from other people as well as from your own experience, in the same way as you learn science?
★ Do the world religions contradict each other, or are they simply talking about the same God in somewhat different ways?
★ Is God able to speak to you through other people?

7

★ Is the voice of conscience nothing more than what your parents and teachers drummed into you when you were young?
★ Is belief in God simply the result of wish-fulfilment? Is *un*belief a matter of wish-fulfilment?
★ In a truly loving relationship, might it sometimes be necessary to say 'No' to the other person's requests? Might it sometimes be necessary to let them manage on their own for a while? Think of some examples.

8

* Is it possible to *force* someone to love another?
* Why do you think there is evil in the world?
* Do you think there would be more or less evil in the world without religions?
* In order to understand what a word like 'love' means, is it necessary to be able to point to examples of its opposite?
* Do you agree there can be different kinds of existence?

9

* Without suffering there is no proof of love; do you agree?
* Do you think sex is just about having a good time, or is there more to it than that?
* What kind of person do you think you would become if sometime you have to suffer a lot?
* Are you often grateful for eyesight, hearing, and health, or do you normally take them for granted?
* Do you think that God experienced suffering through Jesus?

10

* Do you think there could be life after death?
* How should belief in an afterlife affect the way you live *this* life?
* What would be your idea of Heaven?
* Is there a Hell? How could it fit in with belief in a loving God?